The *Cartier*
Book of Racing Colours
2004

Published by Pacemaker
A division of Dunwoody Sports Marketing
Newbury, Berkshire

© Copyright 2004
Pacemaker, a division of Dunwoody Sports Marketing
The Litten, Newtown Road, Newbury, Berkshire RG14 7BB
Telephone +44 (0)1635 35566 Fax +44 (0)1635 845811

First published December 2004

All design and origination by Pacemaker

ISBN 0 9549264 0 4 (Hardback edition)
ISBN 0 9459264 1 2 (Leather bound edition)

Acknowledgements
Pacemaker wishes to thank Cartier UK Ltd for their kind sponsorship of
this title, Rupert Mackeson for his inspiration, Weatherbys Group Ltd for
their help and, of course all Racehorse Owners.

Cartier

Santos-Dumont Watch *Cartier*

Foreword

It gives me enormous pleasure to be associated with the Cartier Book of Racing Colours, the first volume of its kind for more than thirty years.

We are very fortunate that European horseracing is the best in the world, with a history full of the giants of the breed and the horses who became legends through their exploits. Among the colours in this book, many will be familiar as those in which our greatest horses assured their place in racing's folklore, while others belong to those who dream of owning the next Arkle, the next Nijinsky or the next Park Top.

Cartier's own involvement with the 'Sport of Kings' goes back to 1988, the year of the inaugural running of the Cartier Million race at Phoenix Park. Since 1991 the Cartier Awards have come to recognise the champions of the recent chapters of racing history, and the opening section of this book celebrates the ultimate in racing achievement, both human and equine.

Owning a racehorse remains a supreme luxury, and choosing one's colours allows owners to personalise their involvement with this great sport. Nothing quite matches the thrill of seeing a horse ridden by a jockey in colours one has chosen, and we are all lucky to be participants in a sport with so diverse a range of colours in its livery.

I hope that the images in this book evoke memories of cherished moments spent on the racecourse and inspire dreams of glories still to come.

Arnaud M Bamberger

Arnaud M Bamberger
Managing Director
Cartier UK Ltd.

Introduction

Colours are an essential part of the racing scene, and for the most obvious of reasons. Without them, hardly anyone would have any idea about what was happening.

An owner or trainer could no doubt recognise their horse from his looks and his action, and their jockey from his style, though this can hardly be done at long range, but the vast majority of spectators would have no idea and the judge's job would be impossible.

As well as their practical purpose, colours add to the glamour of the sport. There is something especially exciting about a host of jockeys, all in different sets of silks, fighting out a finish in a brilliant clash of blues and yellows and of blacks and reds.

Colours were first used when organised racing was in its infancy, around the middle of the 18th century, and it was in 1762 that the first register of colours was compiled.

The first volume of what had been registered, compiled by Weatherbys, was produced in 1780, and it was in 1887 that such registration of "colours worn by riders" became compulsory.

Even so, there were loopholes and it was possible in certain circumstances in which it was possible to run a horse without having registered colours with the authorities. One firm who compiled racecards for the courses which they managed kept what was called the "Digger's Book", in which they recorded the colours used by some owners who had not registered and were thus saved a fine as long as they arrived on the racecourse with the same set as was described on the racecard.

That cannot happen any longer. Since the introduction of compulsory registration of owners, they have to have colours as well. Today you cannot present yourself in front of the clerk of the scales saying that your colours are "biscuit, tin hat" as one did in the 1950s.

When that first list of colours was organised in 1762, there were 18 names on it, all but two of them titled. Only one remains in its original format — the straw of the Duke of Devonshire and his successors, which were carried to victory by Bachelor Duke in this year's (2004) Irish 2,000 Guineas.

Not many of the owners' families of that long ago day are still involved, either, though Lord Grosvenor's family is that of the Dukes and Duchesses of Westminster, and the Earl of March is chairman of Goodwood. The Dukes of Ancaster and Bridgwater, and the Earls of Northumberland and Waldegrave, do not play much part nowadays.

There are now around 18,000 sets of colours lodged at Weatherbys — about one thousand times that original number. This reflects the huge increase of the number of horses in training (17,000-odd) in the 2004 edition of Horses in Training, which does not include those of Godolphin, Mark Johnston and John Gosden.

It also indicates the number of horses that are owned in partnership, where connections may want to run the horse or horses in the name of a different owner each year. Each owner needs to have his own set. In 2003 alone, there were some 3,000 new registrations added to the list.

Until 1953 it was possible to have colours registered for life, which meant just a one-off payment instead of an annual fee. It now costs £32.39 to record colours on a yearly basis, and you may register as many sets as you like, which is obviously necessary for those like members of the Maktoum family, who may have more than one runner in the same race.

For many years is was possible to have almost any variety of any colour you liked, and over the years, owners have enjoyed schemes like butcher blue, terracotta, eau de nil and drab as varieties from the norm.

Now there are just 18 (coincidentally that number again) from which owners can choose and the most popular among those is royal blue. The most popular accompanying colour is yellow and those at Weatherbys, who are responsible for organising new sets, know that they will have a job on their hands if a new owner says that he or she wants silks with that combination.

Probably the least popular is grey, whose very colour makes it hard to pick out at distance – not much point in having colours if you cannot see them.

There are, though, plenty of varieties of design which can help to cope with the problem. Jackets and/or sleeves can have seams, braces, epaulettes, single or multiple diamonds, a chevron or chevrons or a diabolo, among others. They can be striped, hooped, halved or quartered, be checked or spotted.

The diabolo, which consists of four equally sized triangles, usually of two colours, is one of the more recent additions to the list of eligible designs, but you are no longer allowed horizontal halves (the lower half is obscured inside the jockey's breeches), or out-of-the-way logos like question marks.

It is possible to buy colours which have already been registered at auction, and a few years ago Weatherbys organised sale of single-colour silks, which were called cherished colours and which produced some very high prices.

As an illustration of that, a set of lime green silks was part of an auction which was held at Sothebys in November 2004 and they were expected to make between £30,000 and £50,000! A quite staggering sum when compared with the annual registration fee.

Just looking at the pictures in this Cartier Book of Racing Colours is a fascinating exercise. No wonder seeing them on active service adds so much to the thrill of a race.

GEORGE ENNOR

Note; Historic colours are indicated with (H)

Jacket

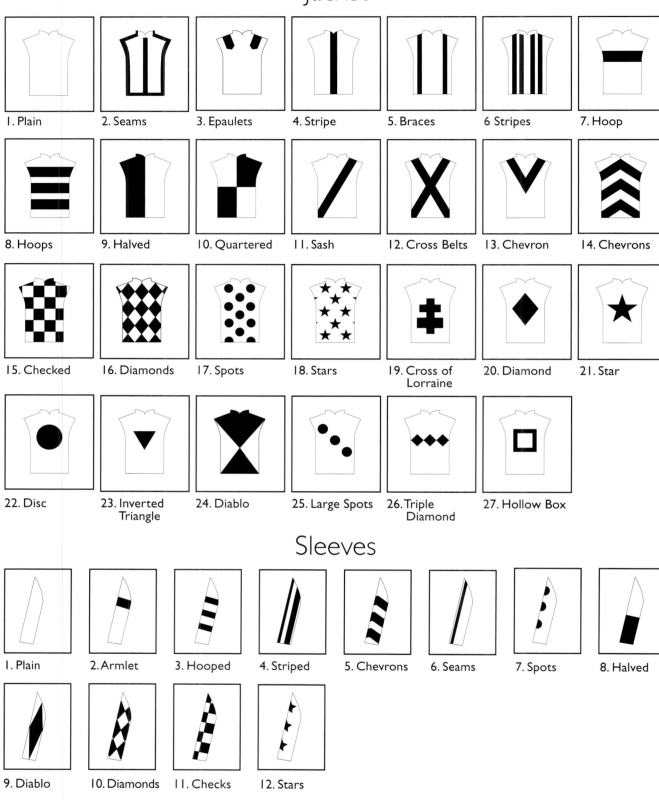

1. Plain
2. Seams
3. Epaulets
4. Stripe
5. Braces
6 Stripes
7. Hoop

8. Hoops
9. Halved
10. Quartered
11. Sash
12. Cross Belts
13. Chevron
14. Chevrons

15. Checked
16. Diamonds
17. Spots
18. Stars
19. Cross of Lorraine
20. Diamond
21. Star

22. Disc
23. Inverted Triangle
24. Diablo
25. Large Spots
26. Triple Diamond
27. Hollow Box

Sleeves

1. Plain
2. Armlet
3. Hooped
4. Striped
5. Chevrons
6. Seams
7. Spots
8. Halved

9. Diablo
10. Diamonds
11. Checks
12. Stars

Caps

1. Plain
2. Hooped
3. Striped
4. Checks
5. Spots
6. Quartered
7. Star
8. Diamond
9. Stars
10. Diamonds

Colours Chart

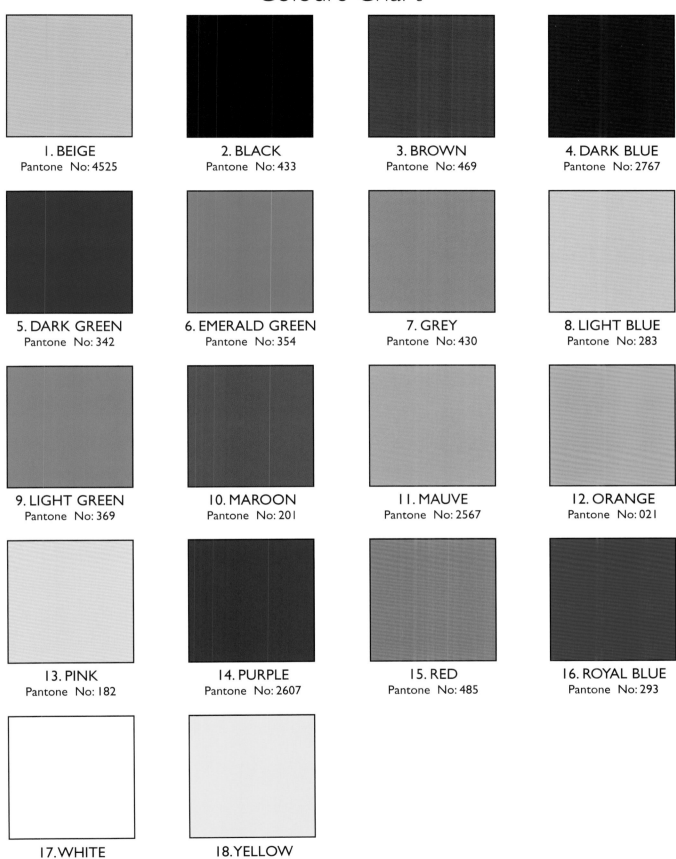

1. BEIGE
Pantone No: 4525

2. BLACK
Pantone No: 433

3. BROWN
Pantone No: 469

4. DARK BLUE
Pantone No: 2767

5. DARK GREEN
Pantone No: 342

6. EMERALD GREEN
Pantone No: 354

7. GREY
Pantone No: 430

8. LIGHT BLUE
Pantone No: 283

9. LIGHT GREEN
Pantone No: 369

10. MAROON
Pantone No: 201

11. MAUVE
Pantone No: 2567

12. ORANGE
Pantone No: 021

13. PINK
Pantone No: 182

14. PURPLE
Pantone No: 2607

15. RED
Pantone No: 485

16. ROYAL BLUE
Pantone No: 293

17. WHITE

18. YELLOW
Pantone No: 101

NOTE: The Stewards of the Jockey Club have given instructions that colours registered under the Orders and Rules of Racing must be confined to the basic colours and designs set out above and overleaf.
For further guidance on selecting colours please contact Weatherbys.

Cartier Award Winners

Godolphin

Three Year Old Filly	1994	Balanchine
Older Horse	1996	Halling
Two Year Old Colt	1998	Aljabr
Three Year Old Filly	1998	Cape Verdi
Stayer	1998	Kayf Tara
Older Horse	1998	Swain
Stayer	1999	Kayf Tara
Older Horse	1999	Daylami
Horse Of The Year	1999	Daylami
Stayer	2000	Kayf Tara
Older Horse	2001	Fantastic Light
Horse Of The Year	2001	Fantastic Light
Three Year Old Filly	2002	Kazzia
Older Horse	2002	Grandera

Sheikh Mohammed

Hurdler	1992	Royal Gait
Three Year Old Filly	1993	Intrepidity
Older Horse	1993	Opera House
Three Year Old Colt	1994	King's Theatre
Stayer	1994	Moonax
Older Horse	1994	Barathea
Horse Of The Year	1994	Barathea
Two Year Old Filly	1995	Blue Duster
Two Year Old Filly	1997	Embassy

Mr M. Tabor & Mrs John Magnier

Sprinter	1999	Stravinsky
Two Year Old Colt	2001	Johannesburg
Sprinter	2001	Mozart

Mr. M. Tabor

Two Year Old Colt	1999	Fasliyev
Three Year Old Colt	1999	Montjeu
Two Year Old Colt	2002	Hold That Tiger

Mrs John Magnier & Mr M.Tabor

Horse Of The Year	2000	Giant's Causeway
Three Year Old Colt	2001	Galileo
Two Year Old Colt	2003	One Cool Cat

Mr K. Abdulla

Two Year Old Colt	1992	Zafonic
Three Year Old Colt	1993	Commander In Chief
Two Year Old Colt	1997	Xaar
Three Year Old Filly	1997	Ryafan
Three Year Old Filly	2001	Banks Hill
Sprinter	2003	Oasis Dream

Mr J.C. Smith

Sprinter	1993	Lochsong
Horse Of The Year	1993	Lochsong
Sprinter	1994	Lochsong
Stayer	2001	Persian Punch
Stayer	2003	Persian Punch

HH Aga Khan

Three Year Old Colt	2000	Sinndar
Older Horse	2000	Kalanisi
Three Year Old Colt	2003	Dalakhani
Horse Of The Year	2003	Dalakhani

Niarchos Family

Three Year Old Colt	1998	Dream Well
Horse Of The Year	1998	Dream Well
Two Year Old Filly	2002	Six Perfections

Highclere Thoroughbred Racing

Sprinter	1998	Tamarisk
Three Year Old Filly	2000	Petrushka

Cheveley Park Stud

Two Year Old Filly	1994	Gay Gallanta
Two Year Old Filly	2003	Russian Rhythm

Sir Alex Ferguson & Mrs John Magnier

Three Year Old Colt	2002	Rock Of Gibraltar
Horse Of The Year	2002	Rock Of Gibraltar

Lord Carnarvon

Two Year Old Filly	1992	Lyric Fantasy
Two Year Old Filly	1993	Lemon Souffle

Mr W.J. Gredley

Three Year Old Filly	1992	User Friendly
Horse Of The Year	1992	User Friendly

Sprinter	1992	Mr Brooks
Older Horse	1992	Mr Brooks

Mr Paul Green

Three Year Old Filly	1995	Ridgewood Pearl
Horse Of The Year	1995	Ridgewood Pearl

Mrs Anne Coughlan

Three Year Old Colt	1996	Helissio
Horse Of The Year	1996	Helissio

Mr E. Sarasola

Three Year Old Colt	1997	Peintre Celebre
Horse Of The Year	1997	Peintre Celebre

Mr D. Wildenstein

Two Year Old Filly	1998	Bint Allayl
Two Year Old Colt	2000	Tobougg

Sheikh Ahmed Al Maktoum

Two Year Old Colt	1996	Bahamian Bounty
Sprinter	2002	Continent

Lucayan Stud

Three Year Old Colt	1992	Rodrigo De Triano

Mr R.E. Sangster

Two Year Old Filly	1991	Culture Vulture

Mr Christopher Wright

Two Year Old Colt	1991	Arazi

Allen E Paulson

Three Year Old Colt	1991	Suave Dancer

Henri Chalhoub

Stayer	1991	Turgeon

Mr George Strawbridge

Sprinter	1991	Sheikh Albadou

Mr Hilal Salem

Stayer	1992	Drum Taps

Yoshio Asakawa

Chaser	1992	Remittance Man

Mr J.E.H. Collins

Two Year Old Colt	1993	First Trump

Mollers Racing

Stayer	1993	Vintage Crop

Dr Michael Smurfit

Mr E. Scarth	Hurdler	1993	Granville Again
Mr P.D. Savill	Two Year Old Colt	1994	Celtic Swing
Marquesa De Moratalla	Chaser	1994	The Fellow
Saeed Maktoum Al Maktoum	Three Year Old Colt	1995	Lammtarra
Hever Racing Club	Sprinter	1995	Hever Golf Rose
Mr E. Pick	Hurdler	1995	Alderbrook
Wertheimer et Frere	Two Year Old Filly	1996	Pas De Reponse
Mr P Sebagh	Stayer	1996	Nononito

Mr J.N. Yeadon	Chaser	1993	Jodami
Mr D.J. O'Neill	Hurdler	1994	Danoli
Mr Hamdam Al Maktoum	Two Year Old Colt	1995	Alhaarth
Mr R.W. Huggins	Stayer	1995	Double Trigger
Mr Simon Wingfield-Digby	Older Horse	1995	Further Flight
Roach Foods Ltd	Chaser	1995	Viking Flagship
Mr Wafic Said	Three Year Old Filly	1996	Bosra Sham
Mrs A. Head	Sprinter	1996	Anabaa

Stayer	1997	Celeric

Mr Christopher Spence

Sprinter	1997	Royal Applause

Sheikh Maktoum Al Maktoum

Older Horse	1997	Pilsudski

Lord Weinstock

Two Year Old Filly	1998	Torgau

The TT Partnership

Three Year Old Filly	1999	Ramruma

HRH Prince Fahd Salman

Two Year Old Filly	2000	Superstar Leo

The Superstar Leo Partnership

Sprinter	2000	Nuclear Debate

Mr J.R. Chester

Two Year Old Filly	2001	Queen's Logic

Mr Jaber Abdullah

Stayer	2002	Vinnie Roe

Mr Seamus Sheridan

Two Year Old Filly	2003	Attraction

Duke Of Roxburghe

Older Horse	2003	Falbrav

Scuderia Rencati Srl

H. M. The Queen

Cartier

Abbey Racing

Mr Barrie Abbott

Mrs Dan Abbott

Mr Daniel Abbott

Mr Richard Abbott

Mr K. Abdulla

Mr K. Abdulla
(second colours)

Mr Jaber Abdullah

Mr Mitaab Abdullah

Mr Nasser Abdullah

Mr Saeed Jaber Abdullah

Mrs O. Abegg

Mr David J. Abell

Aberdeenshire Racing Club

Aboobaker Harris & Taylor

Mr Michael D. Abrahams

Mr Tony Absolom

Achilles International

Acorn Racing

Action Bloodstock

Hon Robert P. Acton

Mr David Adair

Mr Barry Adams

Mr David M. Adams

Mr David J. Adams

Mrs Pauline Adams

Mr T. L. Adams

Mr Toby H.D. Adams

Lady Addington

Mr G. Addiscott

Mrs J. H. Addison

Mrs J. Addleshaw

Adrienne & Michael Barnett

Adweb Ltd

H. H. Aga Khan

H. H. Aga Khan (second colours)

Miss Z. P. Aga Khan

Mr Hassan Ahamdi

Mr D. M. Ahier

Mr N. G. Ahier

HRH Sultan Ahmad Shah

HRH Sultan Ahmad Shah (second colours)

Dr Jamal Ahmadzadeh

Mr A. Ahmed

Mr J. T. H. Ainslie

Mr Robert Aird

Mr W. M. Aitchison

Lady Aitken

Mr C. Akers

Mr Malih Al Basti

Sultan Al Kabeer

Mr Abdulla Al Khalifa

H E Sheikh R Al Maktoum

H E Sheikh R Al Maktoum (second colours)

Mr Hamdan Al Maktoum

Mr Hamdan Al Maktoum (second colours)

Maktoum Al Maktoum

Maktoum Al Maktoum (second colours)

Mrs Sarah Al Maktoum

Sheikh Ahmed Al Maktoum

Sheikh Ahmed Al Maktoum
(second colours)

Sheikh Hamdan Bin
Mohammed Al Maktoum

Sheikh Mohammed
Obaid Al Maktoum

Mr M. J. Al-Qatami

Mr A. Al-Rostamani

K. Al Said

H H Prince Yazid
Bin Al Saud

Mr Mirza Al Sayegh

Mr Hadi Al-Tajir

Alan Brazil Racing Cub

Lord Albermarle

Miss Elizabeth Aldous

Lady Aldous

Aldridge Racing Limited

Mr Giovanni Alessi

Mrs Hamish Alexander

Mr Jamie Alexander

Mr G. N. Alford

Mr G. Algranti

Mr F. M. Alger

Mr Arashan Ali

Mr Saif Ali

All For One & One
For All Partnership

All Four Corners

All Saints Racing

All The Kings Horses

Mr David Allan

Mr Ivan Allan

Mr John F. Allan

Mrs Yoshiko Allan

Mr Bill Allan

Mr Joe L. Allbritton

Mr D. Allen

Mr Ben Allen

Mr C. N. Allen

Mr F. J. Allen

Mrs Ethel Allen

Mr Nic Allen

Mr S. G. Allen

Mr V. A. Allen

Sarah, Lady Allendale

Allevamento Gialloblu

Mr Austin Allison

Mr D. F. Allport

Mr Roger Allsop

Miss Carolyn A. B. Allsopp

Allsorts

Mr R. Alner

Mr Khalil Alsayegh

Alscot Blue Group

Always Hopeful Partnership

Amaroni Racing

Mr E. J. Alston

Mr Richard Ames

Mr W. Amos

Amwell Racing

Mr Benny Andersson

Mr C. Anderson

Mr Campell Anderson

Mr R. E. Anderson

Mrs D. Anderson

Mr M. Andrew

Mr Anthony Andrews

Mr Bob Andrews

Angmering Park Stud

Mr N. J. Angus

The Earl Annandale &
Hartfell

Annapurna Partnership

Annwell Inn Syndicate

Mrs B. Ansell

Mr P. Ansell

Ansell of Watford
(Bookmakers)

Mr Glen Antill

Antoniades Family

APB Racing

Appleby Lodge Stud

Mr Ben Arbib

Sir Martyn Arbib

Mr D. W. P. Arbuthnot

Ms Ellen Arbuthnott-Rook

Mr Matt Archer

Mr R. J. Arculli

Argent Racing

Major P. Arkwright (H)

Mr D. H. Armitage

Mr A. M. Armitage

Mr Peter Armitage

Mr William Armour

Mrs Robert Armstrong

Army Air Corps

Mr M. Armytage

Mr P. Arnold

Mr R. Arnold

Around The World
Partnership

Mr R. K. Arrowsmith

Mrs Richard Arthur

Ascot Authority

Mr David Ashbrook

Mr D. L. Ashby

Mrs E. Ashby

Mrs M. Ashby

Mrs S. Ashby

Ashley House Racing

Ashley Carr Racing

Ashleybank Investments
Limited

Mr P. Asquith

Mr Nicholas Astaire

Mrs E. M. Astley-Arlington

Aston House Stud

The Hon William Astor

Mr S. M. Atkins

Mr Ron Atkins

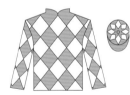

Atkinson Baillie Gill

Atlantic Racing Limited

Atlas International

Mr N. B. Attenborough

Mr B. Auchterlounie

Auldyn Stud Ltd

Mr Jean-Rene Auvray

Avalon Surfacing Ltd

Mrs Linette Avery

Mr M. Avison

Avon Thoroughbreds Ltd

Axminster Carpets Ltd

Axom

Sir James Aykroyd

Mr N. G. H. Ayliffe

Mr J. W. F. Aynsley

Mr A. C. Ayres

Mr D. J. Ayres

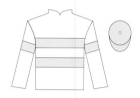

Mr J. Aznar

Mr B. Babbage

Bache Silk

Mr D. H. Back

Mrs Peter Badger

Capt. M. S. Bagley

J. Bagwell-Purefoy

Mr C. Bahadur

Mr A. Bahbahani

Mrs C. Bailey

Mr A. Bailey

Mr A. W. Bailey

Mr E. J. T. Bailey

Mr G. T. H. Bailey

Mr K. C. Bailey

Mr P. Bailey

| Mr P. G. Bailey | Mr Roy Bailey | Mrs Angie Bailey | Major H. A. Baillie | Mr A. J. Baillie |
| Mr Alastair Baillie | Mr N. Baillie | Mr J. R. Bainbridge | Mr R. H. Baines | Mrs Elaine Baines |

| Mrs Joanne Baines | Miss E. J. Baker | Mr L. M. Baker | Mr R. J. Baker | Mrs A. E Baker |

| Mr G. B Balding | Miss Clare Balding | Mr I. A. Balding | Mr John Balding | Mr Peter Balding |

| Mr R. A. Ballin | Ballygallon Stud Ltd | Ballyleah Bloodstock | Ballymacoll Stud | Lady Bamford |

| Miss A. C. Bamford | Bangor-On-Dee Racing Club | Bankhouse Racing | Mr E. J. Banks | Barbara Jamet and Templeton Stud |

Mr Patrick Barbe

Mr Paul K. Barber

Mr R. H.T Barber

Mr Richard Barber

Mr W. G. N. Barber

Mrs Hazel Barber

Mrs S. Barber

Mr C. D. Barber-Lomax

Barcadere Syndicate

Mr R. H. L Barclay

Mrs C. Barclay

Barford Bloodstock

Lt Col T. M. Baring

Mr Nigel Baring

Mr O. Baring

Capt. F. Barker

Mr C. J. B. Barlow

Mr M. H. D. Barlow

Mr T. D. B. Barlow

Sir John Barlow

Susan, Lady Barlow

Major J. R. D. Barnard

Dr Susan Barnes

Mr Rick Barnes

Mr A. Barnes

Mr F. B. Barnes

Mr T. A. Barnes

Mr Mick Barnes

Mr George Barnett

Mr J. L. Barnett

Mr R. Barnett

Barouche Stud Ltd

Mr R. E. Barr

Alan Barraclough

Mrs C. Barratt

Mr A. J. Barrett

Mr Paddy Barrett

Mr D. P. Barrie

Ms K. P. Barron

Mr T. D. Barron

Mr H. Barrons

Mr Denis Barry

Mr J. Barson

Miss C. H. Bartholomew

Brig. G. E. Bartlett

Miss K. A. Bartlett

Bartlett-Dennison-Niven

Mrs M. I. Barton

Mr Robin Barwell

Mrs Annette Barwick

Mr N. Bashir

Basingstoke Commercials

Mr R. E. Baskerville

Lady Elizabeth Basset

Mr M. H. Bastard

Mr Robin Bastiman

Mr Malcolm Batchelor

Mr Andrew Bates

Mr B. Batey

Mr Tom Batey

Mr Jim Bath

Mrs Nigel Batho

Mr C. M. Batterham

Mrs I. Battla

Mr Stan Baugh

Miss S. E. Baxter

Mr F. K. Baxter

Mrs R. Baxter

Bayard Racing

Baydon House Stud

Miss M. Bayliss

Mr A. Bayman

BBB Computer Services

Mr Mike J. Beadle

Mr T. R. Beadle

Mr Ian N. Beale

Mr Andy Beard

The Beare Family

Mr David J. Bearman

Mr Peter Beaton-Brown

Duke of Beaufort

The Hon
Mrs M. H. Beaumont

The Lady Beaverbrook

Mr Robert Beckett

Mrs Ralph Beckett

The Hon W. E. Beckett

Beckhampton Stables Ltd

Mr John Beckwith (H)

Mr T. A. Beddoes

Mr G. H. Beeby

Mr H. G. Beeby

Beechgrove Stud

Mr N. L. Beesley

Mrs P. Beeston

Mr T. Begley

Mr Salem Bel Obaida

Mr Michael Bell

Mr P.T. Bell

Mrs Sue Bell

Mr H. C. Bellingham

Belstane Racing Partnership

Beluga Bay Partnership

Mr & Mrs I.H. Bendelow

Mr Paolo Benedetti

Col Sir Piers Bengough

Mr A. N. C. Bengough

Benham Racing

Mr P. Bennett-Jones

Mr C. J. Benstead

Lady Anne Bentinck

Mr Dave Breakspear

Mrs Caroline
Beresford-Wylie

Berkshire Commercial
Components Ltd

Bermuda Wrectangle Ltd

Bernard Gover Bloodstock
Trading Ltd

Mr J. Bernstein

Mr Richard Berry

Mr J. Berry

Mr Alan Berry

Mr John Berry

Berry Racing

Best Bloodstock

Best Bloodstock
Racing 2003

Mr J. D. Bethell

Mr W. A. Bethell

Mrs James Bethell

Mr John Beveridge

Bewley's Hotels, Glasgow
(BSH Ltd)

Mrs C. J. Bibbey

Bickerton Racing
Partnership

Mr T. W. Biddlecombe

Mr Freddy Bienstock

Bigwigs Bloodstock

Mrs J.F. Billington

Mr G. Bingham

The Hon Miss Charlotte
Bingham

Mr M. Binnington (H)

Mrs T. Binnington

Birch & Pines Syndicate

Mr G. H. L. Bird

Birdstown Syndicate

Miss Diana Birkbeck

Mr Edward Birkbeck

Mrs J. N. Birt-Llewellin

Mr K. Bishop

Bix Racers

Mr A. G. Black

Mr W. M. G. Black

Black Horse Racing Club

Black Sheep Racing

Black Star Racing

Mrs David Blackburn

Mrs Philip Blacker

Blackham, Gould, de Giles (H)

Mr James Blackshaw

Mrs D. E. Blackshaw

Mrs G. S. Blackwell

Mr N. Blair

Mrs T. M. Blair

Blake Kennedy Partnership

Lady Bland

Mr M. Blandford

Mr C. Blank

Blenheim Bloodstock

Mr C.T. Bletsoe

Mr N. M. Bloom

Bloomsbury Stud

Mr Danny Bloor

Mr Derrick Bloy

Blue Lion Racing

Mr R. M. Bluck

Blue Peter Racing

Bluefish Racing

Miss S. Blumberg

Mrs A. C. Blundell

Blush Syndicate

Lady Blyth

Mr Norman. A. Blyth

Mr Martin Boase

Bodfari Stud Ltd.

Mr A. E. Bodie

Mr P. F. Boggis

Ms Fiona Bolger

Mrs J.S. Bolger

Mrs Rosemary Bolt

Lord Bolton

Bolton Grange

Mr R. Bond

Mrs M. J. Bone

Bonnycastle, Hanson,
Harrison, Morton

Bonusprint

Mr J. M. Boodle

Mr C. B. B. Booth

Mr C. W. Booth

Mr Colin G. R. Booth

Border Rail & Plant Limited

Hon J. Borwick

Mr J. R. Bosley

Mr M. R. Bosley

Mrs Bruce Bossom

Mr M. J. Bossom

Mr J. R. Bostock

Mr John Boswell

Mr C. H. Bothway

Bottisham Heath Stud

Mr P. Bottomley

Boundary Garage
(Bury) Limited

Mr T. A. Bourne

Mrs A. D Bourne

Mrs Lucy Young Boutin

Sir Nicholas Bowden

Mr R. W. L. Bowden

Dr K. W. J. Bowen

Mr T. S. Bowlby

Mrs Amanda Bowlby

Mr F. R. Bown

Mr S. R. Bowring

Mr A. Boyd-Rochford

Rosemary, Viscountess Boyne

Mr J. Edward Boynton

Boysaday Racing

Mrs R. Brackenbury

Mr Alan Brackley

Mr Chris Bradbury

Mr J. C. Bradbury

Mr J. M. Bradley

Mr Mark Bradley

Mr Mark Bradstock

Mr D. F. Bradstock

Miss M. Bragg

Mr D. H. Brailsford

Mrs G. M. Brake

Mrs S. A. Bramall

Mr S. T. Brankin

Mrs Shirley Brasher

Braveheart Racing

Mr G. C. Bravery

Mr D. Bray

Mrs J. Breeden

Brendan W. Duke Racing

Mr Michael Brennan

Mr O. Brennan

Mrs Pat Brennan

Mr B. R. Brereton

Mrs A. Brewer

Brian Gubby Ltd

Mr Ian Brice

Mr J. J. Bridger

Mr D. G. Bridgewater

Mrs Gail Bridgewater

Brigadier Racing 2000

Brightling Folly Partnership

Brighton Racing Club

Mr Mark Brisbourne

Lord Bristol

britishhorseracing.com

Mr C. E. Brittain

Mr Mel Brittain

Britton House Stud Ltd

Mr D. I. Broadbent

Mr T. Broderick

Mrs Angela Brodie

Lady Susan Brooke

Mr Edward Charles Brooke

Brooklands Racing

Mr D. L. Brooks

Mr T. L. Brooks

Mr S. A. Brookshaw

Mr D. R. Brotherton

Mr Roy Brotherton

Mrs D. R. Brotherton

Mr Martin Broughton

Broughton Thermal
Insulation

Mr J.T. Brown

Mr D.A. Brown

Mr W.J. Brown

Mr Colin Brown

Mr G. S. Brown

Mr Hector H. Brown

Mr Simon Brown

Mr T. Brown

Mr J. C. Browne

Mr Jim Browne

Mrs Monique V.
Bruce Copp

Bruce Partnership

Mr T. M. Brudenell

Mrs T. Brudenell

Mrs D. Brudenell-Bruce

Sir Gordon Brunton

Mrs M. O. Bryant

Mr M. Bryant

Mr Colin Bryce

Mrs Melba Bryce

Mr P.R. Buckfield

Buckingham Thoroughbreds

Mr C.C. Buckley

Mr M. A. Buckley

Mr Michael Buckley

Sir Roger Buckley

Buckram Oak Holdings

Mr A.F. Budge

Mrs A. F. Budge

Mr A. M. Budgett

Mr C. M. Budgett

Builders Bobby

Mr A. W. Buller

Mr Simon Bullimore

Mrs W. H. Bulwer Long

Capt. T. Bulwer-Long

Mr Nigel Bunter

Mr P. Burdett

Mr D. Burgess

Mr R. Burgess

Mr A. P. Burgoyne

Mr D. J. Burke

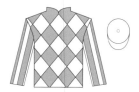

Mrs Valda Burke

Mr B. R Burke

Burley Appliances Ltd

The Earl Of Burlington

Captain Francis Burne

Mrs L. Burnet

Lady Burnham

Mr William Burns

Mrs Seamus Burns

Mr A. Burrell

Mrs Ann Burrell

Mrs Mark Burrell

Mr R. Burridge

Mr R. C. Burridge

Miss M. D. Burrough

Mr B. R. H. Burrough

Burton Agnes Bloodstock

Lady Mairi Bury

Mr J. H. C. Bush

Mr N. Bush

Bush Syndicate

Executors Of The Late
Dowager Lady Bute

Mr David M. Butler

Mr Ron Butler

Sir Kenneth Butt

Mr W. J. Butt

Lady Butter

Mr T. Butterfield

Mrs B Butterworth

Mr A. Buxton

Mr N. M. Bycroft

Byculla Thoroughbreds

Miss Gillian Byrne

Mr A. J. Byrne

Mr David Byrne

Mr R. Byron-Scott

C.R. Marks (Banbury)

Mr M. Caborn-Waterfield

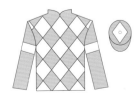

Mr R Cabrera-Vargas

Mr Peter Cadbury

The Earl Cadogan

The Earl Cadogan
(second colours)

Mrs C. J. Cadwaladr

Caerphilly Building
Supplies Ltd

Mr Bill Cahill

Mr J. A. F. Cairns

Mr T. H. Caldwell

Mr W. L. Caley

Miss M. F. Callaghan

Mr A. Callaghan

Mrs J. Callaghan

Mr J. D. Callow

Mr James Callow

Mr S. Callow

Mrs C. Calver

Calvert Carpets

Mr M. Calvert

Calypso Racing

Miss Julie Camacho

Mrs S. Camacho

Lt-Col Colin Cambell

Mr B. R. Cambidge

Mrs T. A. Cambidge

Mr Ian Cameron

Mr Robbie Cameron

Mr W. O. H. Cameron

The Hon Mrs C. Cameron

Mrs H. A. Cameron-Rose

Mr J. W. D. Campbell

The Hon Mrs Nicole
Campbell

Mrs Patrick Campbell
Fraser

Mr C. C. Campbell Golding

Mrs Mette
Campbell-Andenaes

Mrs Zara Campbell-Harris

Mr A. M. Campion

Mr Henry Candy

Mrs Henry Candy

Mr Brian Cann

Canisbay Bloodstock

Mr Don Cantillon

Mrs Edward Cantillon

Mr Brian D. Cantle

Mr R. Cantoni

Mr John Cantrill

Capricorn Hospitality

Car Colston Hall Stud

Mr K. Carbery

Mrs R. D. Cardiff

Sir Richard Carew Pole

Mr D. N. Carey

Dr Ornella Carlini Cozzi

Mrs L. W. Carlson

Mr J. M. Carlyle

Miss C. J. E. Caroe

Mr Ashley Carr

Mr C. D. Carr

Mr David Carr

Mr J. M. Carr

Mr P. J. Carr

Mrs J. Carr-Evans

Mrs B. J. Carrington

Mr Seamus Carroll

Mrs S. Carsberg

Mr R. M. Carson

Mr W. H. Carson

Mr G. Carstairs

Lady Celina Carter

Mr P. Cartmell

Mr P.T. Cartridge

Mr R. K. Carvill

Mr B. I. Case

Mrs N. K. Case

Case Racing Partnership

Mrs J. Cash

Mr L. Cashman

Casino Racing Partnership

Mr D. H. Caslon

Mr Alberto Casolari

Mr T. Cassidy

Miss Nuala Cassidy

Mr J. M. Castle

Castlemead Developments
Limited

Castlemore Securities
Limited

Castles UK

Countess Cathcart

Mr H. R. C. Catherwood

Mrs Stewart Catherwood

Lord Cathorne (H)

Mr W. F. Caudwell

Mr Mike Caulfield

Lord Cavendish

Cavendish Racing

Mrs Christine Cawley

Mr N. Cawood

Sir Peter Cazalet (H)

Mr G. Cazenove

Cazanove Clear
Heights Racing (H)

Mrs J Cecil

Mr H. R. A. Cecil

Mrs Vanessa Cecil

Cedar Lodge 2000
Syndicate

Celtic Racing

Centaur Racing Ltd

Cereal Partners

Chaddleworth Partnership

Chalfont Foodhalls Ltd

Miss J. A. Challen

Miss Louise Challis

Mr A. J. Chamberlain

Mr N. Chamberlain

Mr T. Chamberlain

Mr E. C. Chamberlayne

Mr M. E. Chamberlayne

Mr G. Chambers

Mrs Peter Chambers

Mr P. R. Chamings

Mr B. J. Champion

Mr Fred Champion

Mr R. W. Champion

Champneys Partnership

Mrs M. Chance

Prof. E. M. Chance

Mrs S. S. Chandler

Mrs Alexandra J. Chandris

Dr Fuk To Chang

Mr M. Channon

Mr David W. Chapman

Mr F. W. W. Chapman

Major D. N. Chappell

Mr N. T. Chappell

Mr T. G. A. Chappell

Mrs Jane Chapple-Hyam

Mr J. F. R. Chapple

Mr P. Charalambous

Mr Maurice Charge

Mr G. F. H. Charles-Jones

Mrs Jessica Charles-Jones

Mr D. Charlesworth

Charlock Stud

Mr A. Charlton

Mr Harry Charlton

Charnock Bates

Charsam Limited

Mr Peter Charter

Charterhouse Holdings Plc

Chartwell Racing

Chasetown Civil
Engineering Ltd

Mrs M. V. Chaworth-
Musters

Chelgate Public
Relations Ltd

Mr Christopher Chell

Lady Chelsea

Chelsea Artisans Ltd

Cheltenham Race Club
Owners Group

Cheltenham Racing Ltd

Chemipetro Limited

Mrs J. A. Chenery

Mr Layton T. Cheshire

Mr J. R. Chester

Mr Patrick Chesters (H)

Lord Chetwode

Cheveley Park Stud

Chevington Stud

Mr J. R. Cheyne

Mr T. C. Chiang

Mr Timothy N. Chick

Mr Brian Chicken

Mr H. A. Chisenale-Marsh

Ms J. Choake

Lady Cholmeley

Mr G. W. Chong

Mrs Susie Chown

Chris & Antonia Deuters

Mr Athos Christodoulou

Mr D. J. Christopher

Christy Partnership

Mr G. C. H. Chung

Mr H. C. Chung

Mrs E. Chung

Miss Vanessa Church

Churchills Ltd

Mr D. G. Churston

Mrs Geoffrey Churton

Capt. D. N. V. Churton

Circular Distributors Ltd (H)

City Industrial Supplies Ltd

City Racing Club

Lady Clague

Mr J. D. Clague

Mr S. J. Claisse

Lady Clanwilliam (H)

Mr D. J. Clapham

Mr A. W. F. Clapperton

Mr W. M. Clare

Clarendon Thoroughbred Racing

Claret & Blue Army

Mr G. N. Clark

Mr J. C. Clark

Mr J. W. P. Clark

Mr M. A. Clark

Mr Martin W. Clark

Mr N. C. Clark

Mr Philip E. Clark

Mr R. J. Clark

Mr Simon N. Clark

Mr W. D. Clark

Lady Clarke

Mr A. Clarke

Mr C. C. Clarke

Mr Derek Clarke

Mr M. J. Clarke

Mr Roger Clarke

Mr S. R. Clarke

Mr Simon W. Clarke

Mr T. Clarke

Mrs C. A. Clarke

Mrs C. M. Clarke

Mrs E. M. Clarke

Sir Stanley Clarke (H)

Mr Geoffrey Clarkson

Classic Gold

Mr Robert N. Clay

Mr W. Clay

Mr C. Clayton

Mr D. G. Clayton

Mr J. A. Clayton

Mrs M. A. Clayton

Clear Racing

Mr Derek D. Clee

Mrs Sylvia Clegg

Mrs C. Clement

Mr I. R. Clements

Mr James Clements

Mr P. J. Cleveley

Mrs L. Cleveley

Mr A. D. Cliff

Mr David Cliff

Mr Brian Clifford

Mrs Irene Clifford

Mr R. L. Clifton-Brown

Lord Clinton

Mr P. L. Clinton

Clipper Group Holdings

Cliveden Stud

Mr E. R. Clough

Mr H. B. B. Clowes

Mr Tim Clowes

Mr M. J. G. Clubb

Lady Sarah Clutton

Mr Nigel Clutton

Coach House Racing

Mr D. S. Coates

Mr Michael Coates

Mr Mick Coburn

The Hon Thomas Cochrane

Lord Cochrane of Cults

Mr A. D. Cockburn

Mr Barry J. Cockerell

Mr B. Cockerill

Mr David Cocks

Dr Frederick W.J. Cody

Mr R. B. Cody-Boutcher

Mrs J. Coghlan-Everitt

Mr Andrew L. Cohen

Mr L. Cohen

Mr Richard J. Cohen

Mr Seymour Cohn (H)

Mr K. A. Coker

Capt. Christopher Coldrey

Mr John Cole

Mr P. F. I. Cole

Mrs P. F. I. Cole

Mr A. J. Coleing

Mr K. F. Coleman

Mr A. R. Coley

Colfax Window
Systems Ltd

Colin Brown Racing II

Colin Davey Racing

Miss E. M. L. Coller

Mr Brian Collett

Miss Jane Collier

Mr James E.S. Colling

Mr H. J. Collingridge

Mr E. E. Collingwood

Mrs E. S. M.
Collingwood-Cameron

Lady Collins

Mr A. K. Collins

Mr B. J. Collins

Mr Ben Collins

Mr J. E. H. Collins

Mr K. E. Collins

Mr Lincoln Collins

Mr Ron Collins

Mr T. Collins

Mr T. H. Collins

Mr Tim Collins

Mr C.I. Collinson

Mrs Isabel M. Collinson

Mr Alex Colquhoun

Mr C. F. Colquhoun

Mr Davis Coltman

Miss Elizabeth Colver

Mr S. E. Colvin

Mr A. P. N. Compton

Mr Stuart E. Compton

Concertina Racing

Conkwell Grange Stud Ltd

Connaught Racing

Lady Connell

Mr J. E. Connell

Sir Michael Connell

Mr J. M. Connolly

Miss B. Connop

Mr John Connor

Mrs Jacqueline Conroy

Mr D. P. Constable

Mr S. Constant

Mr A. J. Conway

Mrs J. Conway

Mrs Thomas Conway

Mr A. J. Cook

Mr M. R. M. Cook

Mr R. Cook

Mr Robert E. Cook

Mrs Pippa Cook

Mr C. J. Cookson

Mrs M. J. B. Cookson

Coombe Wood Racing
Syndicate

Mrs J. Coombs

Mr Brian Cooper

Mr C. W. Cooper

Mr D. C. G. Cooper

Mr D. S. Cooper

Mr G. I. Cooper

Mr G. V. Cooper

Mr Nicholas Cooper

Mr Peter D. Cooper

Mr P. E. Cooper

Mr Robert Cooper

Mrs Diane Christine
Cooper

Mrs Sarah Cooper

Sir Richard Cooper

Miss H.L. Cope

Mrs D. Cope

Mr Anthony D. Copley

Mr M Corbett

Mr P. J. Corbett

Mr R. A. C. Corbett

The Hon Mrs J. M. Corbett

Mr Tim Corby

Mr Simon Cordingley

Coriolan Links Partnership

Coriolis Partnership

Mr C.W. M. Cornelius

Mr R. J. Cornelius

Mr J.A. Cornett

Mr Mike Cornish

Mrs T. Corrigan-Clark

Mr D. J. S. Cosgrove

Mrs Suzanne
Costello-Haloute

Cotswold Racing &
Lambourn Horse

Cotswold Stud

Mr C. Cottingham

Mrs P. M. Cottle

Mrs Rowena Cotton

Mr Rupert Cottrell

Mr A. J. Cottrell

Mr T. O. Coughlan

Mrs Anne Coughlan

Mr Gary Coull

Mr Mick Coulson

Count Calypso Racing

Countrywide Racing

Countrywide Steel
& Tubes Ltd

Mr J. Coupe

Mr C. J. Courage

Mr T. C. Court

Miss S. M. Cousins

Mr E. Cousins

Mr Andrew Coveney

Lady Maria Coventry

Countess Coventry

Mr J. A. Cover

Cover Point Racing

Mr G. M. Cowan

Mr Gordon Cowan

Mrs C. A. Coward

Lord Cowdray

Mr R. Cowie

Mrs Linda Cowl

Mr R. W. Cowley

Mr C. R. Cox

Mr David H. Cox

Mr David Cox

Mr Timothy Cox

Mrs T. L. Cox

Miss Bridget Coyle

Mr R. K. Crabb

Mr Alan G. Craddock

Mr K. Craddock

Mrs K. Craggs

Miss I. E. L. Craig

Mr B. J. Craig

Mr R. J. Crake

Crandon Park Stud

Mr I. P. Crane

Mr Peter M. Crate

Mr N. L. Crawford-Smith

Mrs A. Crawght-Green

Lord Crawshaw

Mrs A. F. B. Crawshaw

Miss J. F Craze

Cree Lodge Racing Club

Mr David Crichton-Watt

Mr J. M. Crichton

Cricket Club Owners
Group (2000)

Major J. R. Crockett

Mrs P. D. Croft

Mr A. D. Crook

Mr C. Crossley Cooke

Mrs E. A. G. Crossley
Cooke

Miss Jo Crowley

Mr R. Crutchley

Cuadra Africa

Mr Richard G. Cuddihy

Mr J. M. Cullinan

Mrs Luca Cumani

Cumbrian Industrials Ltd

Mr P. D. Cundell

Mrs S. Cunliffe-Lister

Mr T. S. M. Cunningham

Mr K. O. Cunningham-Brown

Mr M. Cunningham-Reid

Mrs B. J. Curley

Mrs Peter Curling

Mr T. Curry

Mr T. M. J. Curry

Mr Charles Curtis

Mr T. M. Curtis

The Hon. R.F.N. Curzon

Mr H. A. Cushing

Mr S. H. Cussons

Mr T. A. K. Cuthbert

Mrs Bernice M. Cuthbert

Mr C. A. Cyzer

Mrs Charles Cyzer

D. Goodenough
Removals & Transport

D.R. Gandolfo Ltd

Dab Hand Racing

Dachel Stud

Mr O.P. Dakin

Mr P.C.J Dalby

Mr J.S. Dale

Mr M.L. Dale

Mrs Jenny Dale

Mr P.A. Dales

Mrs Hugh Dalgety

Mr Ian G.M. Dalgleish

Lord Dalmeny

Mr J.N. Dalton

Mrs Heather Dalton

Mr D.J. Daly

Mr M.A.J. Daly

Danebury Racing Stables Ltd

Mrs A. Daniel

Mr J. Daniels

Mrs R.J. Daniels

Danum Racing

Mr John Darby

Mr K.H. Darby

Mr Paul D'Arcy

Mrs Sue D'Arcy

Lord Daresbury

Mr D.W.D. Darling

Mr W. Darling

Mr Paul Darling

Mr R. Darlington

Mrs Sylvia Darlington

Mr V.R.A. Dartnall

Mr B. Dascombe

Mr Khalifa Dasmal

Mrs John Davall

Mrs J.V.C. Davenport

Mr F. Davies

Mr H.J.W. Davies

Mr Mel Davies

Mr O.I.F. Davies

Mr Twelly Davies

Mrs Chris Davies

Dr T.J.W. Davies

Lady Davis

Mr J.G.V. Davis

Mr. Peter N. Davis

Mr Scott H. Davis

Mr Tim Davis

Mr Warwick Davis

Mrs Susan Davis

Sir Peter Davis

Major Paddy Davison

Mrs Gail Davison

Mr R.C. Davison

Mrs A.E. Dawes

Mr M.J. Dawson

Mr Tom Dawson

Mrs A Dawson

Mr A.A. Day

Mr Adam Day

Mr G.E. Day

Mr J.F. Day

Mrs Lee Ann Day

Mr Pete Daykin

Mr Ronnie de Beau-Lox

Mr W. de Best-Turner

Major J.H. de Burgh

Mr H. De Burgh

Miss Helena De Chair

Marc De Chambure (H)

Mr J.A.T. de Giles

Mr Les De La Haye

Lady De La Warr

Lord De La Warr

De La Warr Racing

Mr J. De Las Casas

Mr J. De Lisle Wells

Mr E.P.F. De Plumpton
Hunter

Mr R.T. de Plumpton
Hunter

Sir Evelyn De Rothschild

Mr Nicholas De Savary

Mrs Nicholas De Savary

Mr P. De Vere Hunt

Mr Ian de Wesselow

Mrs L.S.R. de Wesselow

Mr Dennis Deacon

Mr A.J. Deakin

Mr P.A. Deal

Mr F. Dean

Mr Nigel Dean

Mr Richard Dean

Dean Ivory Racing Ltd

Mr Guy Dearman

Mr K. E. Deen

Mr D.J. Deer

Mr P.J. Deer

Mr J.S. Delahooke

Mr Martin Delaney

Mr G. E. Dempsey

Mr Nigel Dempster

Mr Malcolm C. Denmark

Mr D.S. Dennis

Mr D.W. Dennis

Mr Toby E.D. Dennis

Mr W.W. Dennis

Lord Derby

The Countess of Derby

Mr D.F. Desmond

Mr Chris Deuters

Mrs Anne Devine

Mrs M. Devine

The Earl of Devon

Duke of Devonshire

Mrs S. Dewar-Finch

Dextra Lighting Systems

Dhobiwallah Racing

Mrs Sarah J. Diamandis

Mr Peter Diamond

Diamond Racing Limited

Mr Sam Dibb

Mrs R. Dick

Mr A.R. Dicken

Mr F.A. Dickinson

Dig In Racing

Mrs R.E. Digby

Mrs R.P.G. Dill

Mr Robert W. Dilley

Mrs J.D. Dillon

Mrs R.M. Dilnott-Cooper

Mr E.G. Dilworth

Mr F.J. Dilworth

Mr Peter Dimmock

Mr A.B. Dix

Mr Charles Dixey

Mr Paul J. Dixon

Mr M.H. Dixon

Mr R. Dixon

Mrs M.E. Dixon

Mr G.A. Doble

Mr Russell Dobney

Mr D.H.W. Dobson

Mr W.J. Dobson

Mrs P.J. Dobson

Mrs P. Dod

Mrs Peter M. Dodd

Mr J.P. Dodds

Mr G. Doel

Mrs R. Doel

Mr Thomas Doherty

Mr W. Doherty

Mr J.W. Dolby

Domino Racing

Mrs Mo Done

Mrs P. Donner

Lord Donoughmore

Lord Donoughue

Mr Jamie Donovan

Mr P. Donovan

Mr Bobby Donworth

Mr J.G. Dooley

Mr M.A. Dore

H.E. Lhendup Dorji

Mr T.G. Dorrington

Mr V.P. Dorrington

Doubleprint

Mr P.J. Douglas

Douglas, Davis, Urquhart

Miss S. Douglas-Pennant

Mrs D.M. Douglas-Pennant

Mr I. Dowse

Mr J.T. Doyle

Mr K. Doyle

Mr M. Doyle

Mrs Sally Doyle

Sam Doyle

Miss S.J. Doyle

Mr J.L. Drabble

Dragonchain Partnership

Dragon's Stud

Mr D.A. Drake

Mr M.J. Drake

Mr Alan Draper

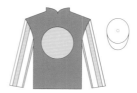

Dream Makers Partnership

Mrs L.M. Dresher

Mr C. Drew

Mr D.H. Driscoll

Mrs J. Druce

Mr D.M. Drury

Mr J.C. Drysdale

Mr Robert Drysdale

Miss I.D. Du Pre

Dubai Thoroughbred
Racing

Mr Brian Duckett

Duckhaven Stud

Mr J. Duckworth

Mr John Duddy

Mr W.E. Dudley

Lady Duff Gordon (H)

Mrs Ann Duffield

Mr Hugh M. Duffy

Mr J.W. Dufosee

Sir William Dugdale

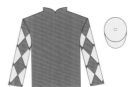

Mr E.P. Duggan

Mr J.D. Duggan

Mr John Duggan

Mr A. Duke

Mr B. Duke

Mr O.R. Dukes

Mr J.M. Dun

Mr Ian Dunbar

Mrs John Duncan

Lady Dundas

Dune Racing

P.J. Dunford

Dr Michael Dunleavy

Mr J.L. Dunlop

Mrs Edward Dunlop

Mr B. Dunn

Mr D. Dunn

Mrs A.J.K. Dunn

Mrs C.J. Dunn

Sir Robin Dunn

Mr David J. Dunne

Mrs V.A.J. Dunne

Mrs Margaret R. Dunning

Mr C.W.W. Dupont

Lord Durham

Mr Danny Durkan

Mr William Durkan

Durkan Limited

Mr R.J. Durrant

Mr H. Dutfield

Mrs Nerys Dutfield

Mr P.C. Dutton

Mrs Janet Dutton

Miss Betty Duxbury

Mr John Dwyer

Mrs Jane Dwyer

Mrs Shelley Dwyer

Mrs J. Dye

Mrs Katie Dyer

Mrs Linda Dyer

Miss C. Dyson

Mr John Dyson

| Miss Caroline Eagle | Eastwell Manor Racing Ltd | Mr W.H. Eastwood | Miss Judy Eaton | Eclipse Thoroughbreds |

Ecosse Racing   Ecurie Pharos   Ecurie Wildenstein   Ecurie Wildenstein (second colours)   Mrs J.E. Eddery

Mr J. Eddings   Mr W.A. Edgington   Mr C.L.A. Edgington   Mr J.L. Eddis   Mr D. Eddy

Mr R.G. Eddy   Mr Charles Eden   Eden Racing   Mr Jeremy Edge   Edingburgh Racing Club

Mrs V.M. Edmondson   Mrs S.K. Edmunds   Mr Neil J. Edwards   Capt E.J. Edwards-Heathcote   Mrs J. Edwards-Heathcote

Mr John W. Egan   Mrs Joan L. Egan   Mr Charles Egerton   Mr N. Eggleston   Mrs S. Egloff

Mr C.P. Eich	Nagy El Azar	Elbrick Estates	Eldon Stud Racing	Miss Shirley Elias
Mr S.F. Eliot	Elite Racing Club	Elite Racing Club (second colours)	Mr Alan C. Elliot	Mr Andrew Elliot

Mr J.M. Elliot	Mr N. Elliot	Mr Nick Elliot	Mr A.P. Ellis	Mr J. Ellis

Mrs A. Ellis	Mrs Angela Ellis	Mrs E.K. Ellis	Ellis Stud Partnership	Mr Brian Ellison

Ellison Racing	Mrs C.J. Ells	Mrs S.P. Elphick	D.S. Elsworth	Mr D.R.C. Elsworth

Mr R.S. Elwell	Mr S.N.J. Embiricos	Mrs S.N.J. Embiricos	Ms A.E. Embiricos	Mrs Jill Emery

Eminence Grice
Partnership

Mr A. Emmerson

Mr N.M. Emmerson

Mrs John Endersby

Mr C. Engelhard (H)

Miss E.M.V. England

Mr David English

Mrs Jean Ennis

Epsom Partnership

Equiname Ltd

Mr David Erwin

Espirit de Corps Racing

Espresso Racing

Countess Marianne
Esterhazy

Estio Racing

Mr Tim Etherington

Mrs A. Eubank

Eureka Racing

Eurolink Group Plc

Mr D.C. Eustace

Mrs James Eustace

Mr Gerald W. Evans

Mr M.A.L. Evans

Mr M.J.M. Evans

Mr Mervyn J. Evans

Mr P.D. Evans

Mr Russell Evans

Mr Steve Evans

Mr W.J. Evans

Mrs Bettine Evans

Mrs R.J. Evans

Mr D. Evatt

Mr D.B. Evatt

Events International Ltd

Mr W.R.J. Everall

Mr M.A. Everard

Mr Patrick Everard

Mr Bill Everett

Major A.M. Everett

Mr G.D. Everett

Mr Mark M. M. Everett

Lady Eyre

Mrs Anne Eyre

Lady Fairhaven

Mr R.G. Fairs

Prince A.A. Faisal

Viscount Falmouth

Mrs G. Fane

Mr James Fanshawe

Mr R.L. Fanshawe

Mrs E. Fanshawe

Mrs J. Fanshawe

Mr Franco Fantoni

Fares Stables

Mrs William S. Farish

Mr W.S. Farish III

Mr W.S. Farish Jnr

Mr J. Farley

Mr Tracy Farmer

Mr Charles Farr

Mr H.J.P. Farr

Mr E.J. Farrant

Mr Frank A. Farrant

Mr Rodger Farrant

Mrs Alison C. Farrant

Mrs Renee
Farrington-Kirkham

Mrs June Fattorini

Mr David Faulkner

The Hon Mrs M. Faulkner

Mr Roberto Favarulo

Favourites Racing

Mr Chilton Fawcett

Mr Tony Fawcett

Fayzad Thoroughbreds Ltd

Mr R.N. Fearnall

Mrs John Fearnall

Mr J.A. Featherstone

Mr J.R. Featherstone

Mr N.K. Featherstone

Mrs Joy Feerick

Mr K.J. Fehilly

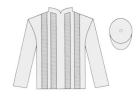

Mrs R.J. Feilden

Ms J.L. Feilden

Felix Rosensteil's
Widow & Son

Mrs S.V. Fellowes

Mrs C.A. Fenaroli

Mrs Christine Fennell

Mrs Joy Fenton

Mr H. Fentum

Mr P.T. Fenwick

Mrs P.T. Fenwick

Mrs S. Fenwick

Mr W. Fenwicke-Clennell

Mr John Ferguson

Mrs C.A. Ferguson

Mrs Elizabeth Ferguson

Mrs J.P. Ferguson

Mr Liam Ferguson

Sir Alex Ferguson (H)

Mr J.G. Fergusson

Fernedge Bloodstock Ltd

Mr P. Fetherston-Godley

Mr H.S. Fetherstonhaugh

Mrs L. Field

Mrs M.J. Field

Fielden Racing

Mrs Sally Fields

Fieldspring Racing

Mr G. Fierro

Mr J.A. Filmer-Wilson

Mr T.P. Finch

Mr A.C. Findlay

Mr John Findlay

Mrs A.J. Findlay

Mrs M. Findlay

Mr P.J. Finn

Mr Tony Fiorillo

First Impressions
Racing Group

First Touch

Miss J. Fisher

Mr David Fisher

Mr Jack Fisher

Mr K.F. Fisher

Mrs M. Fisher

Mr J. Fishpool

Fittocks Stud

Lord John Fitzgerald (H)

Fitzroy Thoroughbreds

Five Horses Ltd

Mrs Heather Flaherty

Mr D.J. Flahive

Mr J.R. Fleming

Mr R.M. Fleming

Miss F.M. Fletcher

Mr A.D.T. Fletcher

Mr Barry M. Fletcher

Mr D.E. Fletcher

Mr Neil Fletcher

Mr Noel Fletcher

Mr Richard Fletcher

Mr Steven J Fletcher

Mr Tony Fletcher

Mrs G. Fletcher

Mrs K.E. Fletcher

Mr J. Flint

Mr J.L. Flint

Mr Gary Flitcroft

Mr R.M. Flower

Mr R.M. Flower
(second colours)

Mrs Alyson Flower

Mrs Alyson Flower
(second colours)

Miss Tracey Flynn

Mr Frank Flynn

Mr Mike Flynn

Mr W.W. Flynn

Mr W.P. Flynn

Mr Dennis Patrick Flynn

Mrs H. Focke

Mrs Katherine Fogg

Foley Steelstock

Food Brokers Ltd

Mr M.I. Forbes

Mr Tony Forbes

Mr E.J. Ford

Mr John W. Ford

Mr Richard Ford

Mr Tom Ford

Mr Mel Fordham

Mrs T.A. Foreman

Miss Sandra Forster

Mr D.M. Forster

Mrs Wendy Forster

Mr J.A. Forsyth

Mr R.D. Forsyth

Mr M. Forsyth-Forrest

Mrs C.J. Fortescue

Lady Forwood

Miss C. Foster

Miss J.E. Foster

Mr Nigel Foster

Mr Richard Foster

Mrs J.R. Foster

Mr M.M. Foulger

Four Counties Partnership

Four Of A Kind Racing

Four Seasons Racing Ltd

Fourstar Partners

Mr A. Foustok

Mr John Fowden

Mr H. Fowler

Mrs J. Fowler

Mr John Fowles

Mr Dick Fowlston

Mr C. Fox

Mr I. Fox

Mr R.J. Fox

Mr William Fox

Mr W.O.L. Fox-Pitt

Mrs Oliver Fox-Pitt

Mr Michael A. Foy

Mr A. Frame

Mr J.L. Frampton

Mrs T. Frampton

Mrs Shirley France

Mrs Merrick Francis III

Francome And Friends

Franconson Partners

Mr A. Franklin

Mrs Hugh Fraser

Fraser Miller Racing

Mr David Fravigar

Mr Ian Frazer

Mr S.C. Freedman

Mr J.A. Freeman

Fremel & Friends

Mr John French

Mr Stephen Freud

Sir Clement Freud

Friary Bloodstock
Company Ltd

Lt-Col N.E. Frieze

Mr R.L.W. Frisby

Mr S.R. Frisby

Mr R.J. Froggatt

Miss Jumbo Frost

Mr J.D. Frost

Mr T.C. Frost

Mr C.A. Fuller

Mr J.A. Fuller

Mr Leonard Fuller

Mr R.H.F. Fuller

Mr R.N. Fuller

Mr R.R. Fuller

Mrs Richard Fuller

Mr B.N. Fulton

Mrs A. Fulton

Mrs A.E. Fulton

Mr Jim Furlong

Mr M.J. Furlong

Miss J.M. Furness

Mrs F.W. Furness

Mrs J.W. Furness

Sir Stephen Furness

Mr Josef Fusenich

Mr S. Fustok

Mr Mike Futter (H)

Mr J. Fyffe

Mrs B.H. Fyfe-Jamieson

Fyfield Racing

Mr G.A. Fynn

G. B. Turnbull Ltd

G. B. Partnership

G. R. Bailey Ltd
(Baileys Horse Feeds)

Mr R.A. Gadd

Mrs J. Gadd

Mr Michael H. Gadsby

Mr W. P. Gaff

Mr Tom Gaffney

Mrs K. S. Gaffney

Lord Gainsborough (H)

Gainsborough Stud

Mrs Gail Gaisford

Mr Ziad A. Galadari

The Hon Miss
Heather Galbraith

Mr A. R. M. Galbraith

Mr Tony Gale

Mr J. Gallagher

Gallagher Equine Ltd

Mr Trevor Gallienne

Mrs Barrie Gallop

Mrs Jane Galpin

Mr John Galvanoni

Mrs Ann Galvanoni

Miss R. A. Gambazza

Mrs V. D. Gandola-Gray

Mr F. Gardiner

Mr R. W. Gardiner

Mr Corey M. Gardner

Mr D. V. Gardner

Mr N. H. Gardner

Mr J. E. Garrett

Mr Leslie Garrett

Mr A. S Gaselee

Mr N. A. Gaselee

Mr R.F.U. Gaskell

Gaskell, Maccioni,
Myers & Tregoning

Mr Michael Gates

Mr Alessandro Gaucci

Mr Brian Gee

Mr Colin Gee

Mrs S. M. Gee

Mr Simon Gegg

Mr Derek Gennard

Mr J. A. Gent

Mr Peter Gent

Geoff Hubbard Racing

Capt. J. A. George

Miss K. George

Mr Edward St George

Mr T. R. George

Mrs C. A. B. St George

Mr Kalli Georgiou

Gestut Schlenderhan

Mr V. Y. Gethin

Mr Hamad Al Ghowais

Mr D. H. Gibbon

Mr Robert Gibbons

Mr A. G. Gibbs

Sir Roger G. Gibbs

Mr Gary Gibson

Miss Anthea Gibson
Fleming

Mrs W. H. Gibson Fleming

Gibson, Goddard,
Hamer & Hawkes

Mr D. H. Gichero

Mr Mark Gichero

Mrs N. Gidley Wright

Mr Michael Gifford

Mr Reg Gifford

Mrs J. T. Gifford

Gigginstown House Stud

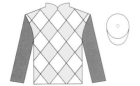

Mr Allan Gilchrist

Mr Jonathan Gill

Mrs J. Gill

Dr Anne J. F. Gillespie

Mr F. Gillespie

Mr J.A. Gillett

Mrs Susan Gilmour

Mrs V. Gilmour

Mr G. F. Gingell

Mr M. J. Gingell

Girls on Tour

Girsonfield Ltd

Girsonfield Stud Racing

Mrs M. J. Gittings-Watts

Mrs D. Given

Mr Robert A. Gladdis

Glasgow House Racing
Syndicate

Gleadhill House Stud Ltd

Mr M. Gleason

Glebe House Stud Ltd

Mr Eddie Gleeson

Mr Graham R. Glover

Mr J.A. Glover

Mrs L. R. Godbere-Dooley

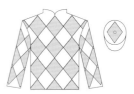

Miss Lorna Goddard

Mr Arthur Goddard

Mrs Linda Goddard

Mr Lionel Godfrey

Mrs Helen Godfrey

Godolphin

Godolphin
(second colours)

Count K. Goess-Saurau

Countess Goess-Saurau

Gold Group
International Ltd

Golden Furlong Racing

Mr J. S. Goldie

Goldie's Friends

Mr B. Goldsmith

Lady Annabel Goldsmith

Mr B.J. Goldsmith

Mr S. Gollings

Mrs Jayne M. Gollings

Mr Raymond Gomersall

Mr Jeremy Gompertz

Mr J. R. Good

Mr Michael Goodbody

Mrs R. Goodbody

Mrs C. M. Goode

Mr Graham Goode

Mr A. A. Goodman

Mr D. J. Goodman

Mrs Patricia Goodman

Goodwood Racehorse
Owners Group

Gordon Franks Training

Miss M. Gordon-Watson

Mr C. Gordon-Watson

Mrs Fiona Gordon

Mrs R. W. Gore-Andrews

Goring Hotel

Mr John H. M. Gosden

Mrs Miles Gosling

Mrs T. Gosling

Mr P. G. Goulandris

Mr Bernard Gover

Mr David Gower

Mr M. J. Grace

Mr Markus Graff

Mr A. B. Graham

Mr Doug Graham

Mr J. D. Graham

Mr N. R. H. Graham

Mr William Graham

Mrs Douglas Graham

Mr A. Graham

Granite By Design Ltd

Mr Chris Grant

Mr John C. Grant

Mr L. P. Grassick

Mr B. M. Gray

Mr Frederick Gray

Mr Peter Gray

Mr R. E. Gray

Mr Robert Gray

Mr A. M. Grazebrook

Great Head House
Estates Ltd

Mr R. E. Greatorex

Mr T. C. O. Gredley

Mr W. J. Gredley

Mr W.J. Gredley
(second colours)

Mrs R. J. Gredley

Lady Green

Mr C. R. Green

Mr Charles Green

Mr David A. Green

Mr Jack Green

Mr R. Lycett Green

Mr M. E. Green

Mr Paul Green

Mr Paul Green
(second colours)

Mr Raymond
Anderson Green

Mr T. A. Green

Mr T. J. Green

Mrs N. J. G. Green

Sir Simon Lycett Green

Hon Mrs J. Greenall

Greenbay Stables Ltd

Greenfield Stud

Major Paul Greenwood

Mr A. Greenwood

Mr J. J. Greenwood

Mr R. E. S. Greenwood

Mr J. M. Greetham

Mr G. G. A. Gregson

Mr Neil Greig

Mrs C. G. Greig

Mrs D. C. Greig

Colonel D.C. Greig

Mr R. Grenville-Webb

Greystoke Stables Ltd

Mr A. P. Griffin

Mr Reg Griffin

Mr G. E. Griffiths

Mr Richard Griffiths

Mr S. G. Griffiths

Mrs E. F. Griffiths

Mrs J. M. Grimston

The Hon G. C.W. Grimston

Lord Grimthorpe (H)

Mr A. Grinter

Mr D. M. Grissell

Lady Jane Grosvenor

Group 1 Racing (1994) Ltd

Mr Rubin Gruber

Grundy Bloodstock Limited

Gryffindor
(www.racingtours.co.uk)

Mr B. M. Guerin

Mr I. Guest

Mr John Guest

Mr Rae Guest

Mr J. L. Guillambert

Mrs P. D. Gulliver

Mr Robert Gunn

Mrs J. J. T. Gunn

Mr Alan Guthrie

Mr J. A. Guthrie

Mr J. S. Gutkin

Gutner E & Krysztoflack
Racing (H)

Mrs Vicki Guy

Mr Douglas Guyer

L. Gvozdenovic

Mr John Hugo Gwynne

Mr D. C. G.
Gyle-Thompson

| H. K. Commissions | Mr J. T. Habershon-Butcher | Mrs Monica Hackett | Mrs Nan Hacking | Mrs J. Hadden-Wight |

| Mr A. Hadjioannou | Mr B. Haggas | Mr M. R. Haggas | Mr R. Haggas | Mrs M. M. Haggas |

| Mr W. J. Haggas | Mr W. J. Haggas (second colours) | Miss V. Haigh | Mrs A. J. Haigh | Mr G. Haine |

| Mrs Diana Haine | Mr W. V. Haines | Miss L. Hales | Mr J. Hales | Halewood International Ltd |

| Mr J. M. F. Halford | Lady Halifax | Lord Halifax | Lord Halifax (second colours) | Mr Peter Hall |

| Hall Farm Racing | Dr A. Haloute | Mr Elias Haloute | Mr D. A. Halsall | Mr G. A. Ham |

Mr Richard Hambro

Mr Rupert Hambro

Mrs R. E. Hambro

Mr C. M. Hamer

Hamilton House Limited

Hamilton Park Members Syndicate

Mr B. P. Hammond

Mr M. D. Hammond

Mr Michael A. Hammond

Mrs Alex Hammond

Mr J. Hammond

Capt T. F. J. Hanbury

Major Christopher Hanbury

Mrs Christopher Hanbury

Mr B. Hanbury

Mr E. R. Hanbury

Mrs Ben Hanbury

Mrs M. A. Hanbury

Mr Jeremy Hancock

Mr Arthur B. Hancock III (H)

Mr Reg Hand

Mr Richard Hand

Mr John Hanmer

Sir John Hanmer Bt

Mr R. Hannon

Mr T. Hannon

Mrs J. A. Hannon

Mr J. Hanson

The Hon Robert Hanson

Mrs B. Harcourt-Wood

Mrs J. A. S. Hardcastle

Mr R. L. Harding

The Hon Miss D. Harding

Lady Hardy

Sir Richard Hardy

Mr Chris Hardy

Mr I. Harland

Harlequin Racing

Harlequin Software
Consultants

Mr J. E. Harley

Mr C. J. Harper

Mr Simon Harrap

Lt-Col E. K. Harries

Mr E. L. Harries

Mr W. C. Harries

Lady Harrington

Lord Harrington

Lady Harris

Major J. D. Harris

Mrs A. E. Harris

Mr H. R. Harris

Harris, Clark,
Swinburn & Harris

Lady Harrison

Mr Neil Harrison

Mr Ray Harrison

Mr S. J. Harrison

Mrs Pat Harrison

Mr S. R. Harrison

Major N. J. Harrison

Mr W. A. Harrison-Allan

Mr B. Harrison-Burcombe

Harry Dunlop
Racing Partnership

Miss D. M. Hartigan

Mr G. C. Hartigan

Lord Hartingdon (H)

Miss Freya Hartley

Mr O. R. M. Hartley

Ms A. Hartley

Mrs P. A. H. Hartley

Mr H. F. Craig Harvey

Mrs Belinda Harvey

Mrs G. Harwood

Mrs M. J. Harwood

Mr P. C. Haslam

Mrs V. Haslam

Mrs Wendy Haslam

Mrs P. Hastings

Sir Stephen Hastings

Mr S. Hastings-Bass

Mr Bernard Hathaway

Hatta Bloodstock
International Ltd

Havelock Racing

Mr N. J. Hawke

Mr J. Hawkins

Mr K. R. W. Hawkins

Mr Tim Hawkins

Mrs B. M. Hawkins (H)

Mr D. Haydn-Jones

Mrs E. M. Haydn-Jones

Haydock Park National
Hunt Partnership

Mr J. W. Haydon

Mrs Brendan Hayes

Mr J. Hayes

Mrs Denis Haynes

Mrs H. E. Haynes

Major J. R. Hayward

Mr Tony A. Hayward

Lady Hayward (H)

Mr Alec Head

Viscount Head

Headquarters Partnership

Mr A. Heaney

Mr J. Heaney

Mr S.R.J. Heaney

Heart of the South Racing

Mr A. M. Heath

Mr Christopher Heath

Mr D. Heath

Mr Robert Heathcote

Mr W. Heathcote

Mr Mark Heaton

Mrs Alan Heber-Percy

The Hon Mrs A. E.
Heber-Percy

Mr Richard Hedditch

Mr P. R. Hedger

Mrs L. Hedlund

Heeru Kirpalani Racing

Mr Patrick Heffernan

The Hon Mrs D. Heimann

Mrs H. J. Heinz

Mr A. S. Helaissi

Helena Springfield Ltd

Mr Joseph Heler

Hellwood Stud Farm

Mr B. G. Hellyer

Mrs E. G. Hellyer

Mr T. M. Hely-Hutchinson

Mr Robert Hemmings

Mr Trevor Hemmings

Mr Trevor Hemmings
(second colours)

Lord Hemphill

Mr S.D. Hemstock

Mr H. Henderson

Mr N. J. Henderson

Mrs John Henderson

Mr Mohammed Bin Hendi

Mr M. Henriques

Mrs R. Henry

Mr Ivor Herbert

Mrs Sarah Herbert

The Hon H. Herbert

Mrs W. R. Hern (H)

Lady Herries

Mr John Hersey-Walker

Hertford Offset Limited

Mr T. W. Heseltine

Hesmonds Stud

Mr John Hetherington

Mr J. Hetherton

Mr A. J. Heyes

Mr Michael Heywood

Mr P. W. Hiatt

Mr Dick Hibberd

Mr P. M. L. Hibbert-Foy

Miss E. Hickey

Mr C. R. Hickey

Mr Andrew Hickman

Mr J. C. Hickman

Mr P. J. Hickman

Mr Richard Hickman

Mrs D. M. Hickman

Mr J.C.S. Hickman (H)

Mr David Hicks

Mr M. E. S. Higgin

Mr C. G. Higgins

Mrs D. J. Higgins

Mr B. Higham

Highclere Thoroughbred
Racing

Highclere Thoroughbred
Racing (second colours)

Mr K. Higson

Mr Mohammed Hilal

Mr J. Ward Hill

Mr Martin Hill

Mr B. W. Hills

Mr Charles Hills

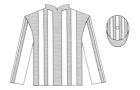

Mr J. W. Hills

Mrs B. W. Hills

Mrs J. Hills

Mrs M. Hills

Mr P. A Hill-Walker

Mr I. C. Hill-Wood

Mrs Mandy Hinchcliffe

Mrs Tim Hinde

Mr J. J. Hindley (H)

Mrs C. H. Hindley

Mrs S. Hindley

Mr Frazer Hines

Mr Yue Yun Hing

Mr Felipe Hinojosa

Hintelsham AB Partners

Hintelsham Cree Partners

Hintelsham DS Partners

Hintelsham SPD Partners

Hintelsham Thoroughbreds

Mr Tony Hirschfeld

Mrs J. L. Hislop (H)

Hislop, Exors Of The Late
Mr J. L.

Mr J. C. Hitchins

Mr N. J. Hitchins

Mrs K. Hitchins

Mr R. P. C. Hoad

Mrs Julie Hoad

Mr A. L. Hobbs

Mr A. R. C. Hobbs

Mr P. D. Hobbs

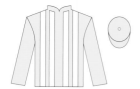

Mr P. J. Hobbs

Mrs S. L. Hobbs

Mrs C. Hobbs

Dr J. A. E. Hobby

Mrs Joy Hobby

Mr W. D. Hockenhull

Mr J. G. Hodder

Mr Alastair Hodge

Mr A.H.B. Hodge

Mr R. J. Hodges

Mrs M. Hoey

Mr & Mrs A. Hogarth

Hogarth Racing

Hoh Oilfield
Services Limited

Mr Richard Hoiles

Mr T. G. Holdcroft

Derek & Cheryl Holder

Mr Andy Holder

Mr S. F. Holder

Mr Pete Holder

Mr Pete Holder
(second colours)

Mrs J Holder

Mr N. J. Holdsworth

Holistic Racing Ltd

Mr T. D. Holland-Martin

Mrs E. Holland-Martin

Mrs J. M. Hollands

Mr L. B. Holliday

Mr A. Hollingsworth

Mr Mark Hollingsworth

Mr A. N. Hollinshead

Mr R. Hollinshead

Mrs L. A. Hollinshead

Dr John Hollowood

Mrs Claire Hollowood

Mrs Anne V.
Holman-Chappell

Mr Simon Holt

Homebred Racing

Mr Saleh Al Homeizi

Mr F. Homer-Morris

Dr Johnny Hon

Hong Kong Cricket Club

Honourable Artillery
Company

Ms Rachel D. S. Hood

Mr F. Hope

Mrs N. Hope

Mr S.R. Hope

The Earl Hopetoun

Mr C.A. Horgan

Mr James Horgan

Mr Jim Horgan

Mr Archie Hornall

Mr Mark Horne

Mrs Mark Horne

Miss L. Horner

Mr P.A. Horner-Harker

Mrs Sarah Horner-Harker

Mr Peter Horsburgh

Mr M. Hosford-Tanner

Mr Ernie Houghton

Mr George Houghton

Mr Leonard Howard

Mrs B. Howard

Howard Barton Stud

Mr G. Howard-Spink

Mrs V. Howard-Vyse

Mr Dave Howe

Mr S. P. Howe

Mr Michael Howitt

Mr A. Howland Jackson

General Sir Geoffrey Howlett

Mr N. B. F. Hubbard

Mr J. S. Hubbuck

Mrs C. J. Hue Williams

Mr R. W. Huggins

Mr Emlyn Hughes

Mr M. T. Hughes

Mr Paddy Hughes

Mr Rob Hughes

Mr Sebastian F. Hughes

Mr P. Hughes

Mr Saeed Abdullah Humaid

Mr M. C. Humby

Mrs Susan Humphreys

Mrs Philip Humphries-Cuff

Mr C. Harman Hunt

Mr J. T. B. Hunt

Hunt & Co (Bournemouth) Ltd

Mr N. Bunker Hunt (H)

Mr T. Hunter Blair

Lord Huntingdon

Miss Caroline Hurley

Mr Dennis Hutchinson

Mr Maurice Hutchinson

Mr F. A. Hutsby

Mr K. Hutsby

Mr Derek Hyde

Mr Edward Hyde

Mr T. Hyde

Mrs T. P. Hyde

Ian David Limited

Mrs D. Ibbotson

Mr A.J. Ilsley

In The Pink Syndicate

In Touch Partnership

Don Enrico Incisa

Mr Nik H. B. Ingham

Mr Michael H. Ings

Mr Peter Innes

Intersky Corporate Club

Interskyracing.com

Mr M. Ioannou

Iona Equine

Mr A. Irvine

Mr D. Irvine

Mrs J. Irvine

Miss H. M. Irving

Mr L. Irving

Mr Rupert C. Irving

Mrs L. Irving

Mrs S. Irwin

Islanmore Stud

Lady Iveagh

Mr Bill Ivens

Mr D.F. Iveson

Mr Dean Ivory

Mrs J. M. Ivory

Ivy House Racing

Mrs P. Izamis

J Nattrass M Howard
R Fawcett T Fawcett

J. B. R. Leisure Ltd

J. Bernstein & C.A. Green

J. Bernstein & C.A. Green
(second colours)

Mr Mohammed Jaber

Mr G. Jabre

Jack Brown
(Bookmaker) Ltd

Mr David J. Jackson

Mr A. A. W. Jackson

Mr Bill Jackson

Mr C. F. C. Jackson

Mr Norman Jackson

Mr W. J. P. Jackson

Mrs J. A. Jackson

Mr David James

Mr E. James

Mr Keith James

Mr S. W. James

Mrs M. E James

Mr D. James-Duff

Mr A. P Jarvis

Mr H. J. Jarvis

Mr John F. Jarvis

Mr M.A. Jarvis

Mr T. Jarvis

Mr William Jarvis

Mrs Ann Jarvis

Mrs Gay Jarvis

Mrs R. N. Jarvis

Jay Dee Bloodstock Limited

Jebel Ali Racing Stables

Mr J. R. Jenkins

Mrs Wendy Jenkins

Mr Bryan P. Jenks

Mr David Jenks

Mr R. J. Jenks

Mr W. Jenks

Mrs Bryan Jenks

Mrs Richard Jenks

Mrs W. P. Jenks

Mr J. Jenner

Mr Charles Jerdein

Jet UK Limited

Mr H. J. Joel (H)

Mr Stanhope Joel (H)

Jobs Racing

John Humphreys
(Turf Accountant)

John Nicholls (Banbury)
Ltd

John Wilding Promotions

Mrs Margaret Johnsey

Johnsey Estates (1990) Ltd

Mr D. A. Johnson

Mr I. K. Johnson

Mr M. R. Johnson

Mr P. Johnson

Mr D.V. Johnson

Mrs Joy Johnson

Mr Mark Johnson

Mr C.R. Johnson

Mr R. F. Johnson Houghton

Mrs R. F. Johnson Houghton

Miss E. Johnson Houghton

Mr G. C. Johnston

Mr A. D. Jones

Mr D. G. Jones

Mr Fergus Jones

Mr J. F. Jones

Mr J. T. Jones

Mr M. G. Jones

Mr N. J. Jones

Mr L. Neil Jones

Mr P. A. Jones

Mr Peter Jones

Mr S. D. Jones

Mr Simon Jones

Mrs Solna Thomson Jones

Dr G.M. Thelwall Jones

Mr D. F. Jordan

Mr F. Jordan

Mr G. Jordan

Mrs M. Jordan

Mr Jack Joseph

Mr K. P. Joseph

Miss Alison Joy

Joy & Valentine Feerick

Mr T. Joyce

Jubert Family

Jumeirah Racing

Jumping Jokers

Juniper Stud Racing

Just Good Fun Club

K. C. Partnership II

Kalani Partnership

Mr Paul Kan

Mrs A. G. Kavanagh

Mrs Maxine Kavanagh

R. E. Kavanagh

Mr D. P. Keane

Mr M. Keane

Mr P. J. Keary

Mrs Jean Keegan

Keen Racing

Geoffrey & Donna Keeys

Mr P. F. Kehoe

Mrs F. Kehoe

Mr J. A. Keighley

Mrs E. Keir

Dorothea, Viscountess
Kelburn

Miss Gay Kelleway

Mr B. J Kelly

Mr Diarmaid Kelly

Mr G. P. Kelly

Mr Peter Kelly

Mr Tim Kelly

Mr John Kelsey-Fry

Kelso Members
Lowflyers Club

Mr R. Kelvin-Hughes

Mr B. C. S Kemp

Mr M.A Kemp

Mr M. N. Kemp-Gee

Mr L. W. Kendall

Mr G. D. Kendrick

Lady Kennard

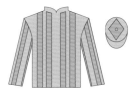

Major & Mrs R. B. Kennard

Mr L. G. Kennard

Mr Ian A. Kennedy

Mr J. P. Kennedy

Kennet Valley
Thoroughbreds

H.R.H Princess Michael
of Kent

Mr F. N. Kent

Lord Kenyon

Mr Michael H. Keogh

Mr R. Keogh

Mr David Ker

Mrs Jeremy Ker

Mr Anthony D. Kerman

Kernow Racing

Mr D. M. Kerr

Mr John Kerr

Mr W. F. Kerr

Mr Michael H. Kerr-Dineen

Mr E. D. Kessly

Mr Simon Keswick

Mrs M. E. Keswick

Sir Chippendale Keswick

Mrs E.A. Kettlewell

Mr H. Key

Mr S. Khaled

Mr Khalid Khalifa
Al Nabooda

Sheikh Ali Abu Khamsin

Mr John Khan

Mr R. N. Khan (H)

Mr Gerald Kidd

Kilboy Estate

Mr Christy Kilgour

Mr Bobby Killoran

Mr Mark Kilner

Mr A. S. Kilpatrick

Mr L. G. Kimber

Lord Kimberley (H)

Mr M. B. J. Kimmins

Mr C. M. Kinane

Mr P.L. Kindersley

Mrs G. Kindersley

Mr A.A. King

Mr J. W. G. King

Mrs A. L. M King

Mr C.O. King

Mrs Brian Kingham

Kings Troop Royal
Horse Artillery

Kingsclere Stud

Kingstone Warren Partners

Kingwood Stud Ltd

Kinloch Arms
(Carnoustie) Ltd

Mr J. M. Kinnear

Kinnersley Optimists

Mrs S. A. J. Kinsella-Hurley

Mr M. V. Kirby

Mr Sylvester Kirk

Dr A. I. Kirkland

Mr L. Kirkwood

Mr H. L. Kirpalani M.B.E.

Mr K. G. Kitchen

Mrs S. Kittow

Mr W. G. Kittow

Lady Lucinda Kleinwort

Mrs Audrey Kley

Miss H. Knight

Mr G. W. Knight

Mr J. R. Knight

Knightsbridge BC

Mr R. F. Knipe

Mrs R. F. Knipe

Miss Linsey Knocker

Mr Anthony Knott

Dr Nigel Knott

Lady Knutsford

Mr J. P. Kok

Mr Ananda Krishnan

Miss A. M. Krysztofiak

Mr M. Krysztofiak (H)

Kuwait Racing Syndicate

Mr R. J. Kyle

Mrs D. A. La Trobe

Mr J. M. Lacey

Ladbrokes Staff Racing Partnership

Mrs Samantha Ladds

Mr David Ladhams

Lady Bamford & The Sangster Family

Lady Blyth

Lady Caffyn-Parsons & Mrs E.E. Dedman

Lady Eliza Mays-Smith

Lady Carolyn Warren & Floors Farming

Lady Whent And Friends

Ladyswood Stud

Ladywood Farm

Lael Stable

Laggan Farm Stud (H)

Mr Stephen Laidlaw

Mr N. W. Lake

Mr Phil Lake

Miss C. Lake

Mrs E. Lake

Sir Freddie Laker

Mr Bob Lalemant

Mr Stephen Lambert

Mr G. Lambton

Mrs S. Lamyman

Mr D. Lancaster-Smith

Mrs J. M. Lancaster

Mr R. J. Lancaster

Mr Ettore Landi

Mrs Jane Lane

Mr R.G. Langley

Miss Audrey Lanham

Mr Bob Lanigan

Larkwood Stud

Mrs Hugo Lascelles

Mr C. Latilla-Campbell

Mr Peter Latilla-Campbell

Miss E. C. Lavelle

Mr R. J. Lavelle

Mrs R. J. Lavelle

Lavender Hill Stud L. L. C.

Thomas Lawn

Mr M.W. Lawrence

Mrs S.J. Lawrence

Mr Robin Lawson

Miss Lawson Johnston

Mrs C. Lawson-Croome

Mr B. L. Lay

Mr J.V. Layton

Mr J.A. Lazzari

Mr A. J. Le Blond

Mr N.H. Le Mare (H)

Mr A. E. Lea

Mr Tim Leadbeater

Mrs H. C. Leader

Mr John Leat

Mrs Ann Leat

Mr R. G. Leatham

Mr Mark A. Leatham

Mr G.H. Leatham

Mr R. R. Ledger

Miss G.T. Lee

Mr F. H. Lee

Mr F.T. Lee

Mr Richard Lee

Mr Paul D. Leech

Mrs S. Leech

Mr N. Lee-Judson

Mr David Lees

Mr John Lees

Mrs C. P. Lees-Jones

Mr C. R. Leetham

Lady Legard

Mr William Legard

Legard Sidebottom & Sykes

Mr P. E. Legge

Mrs Benjamin Leigh

The Leigh Family

Sir Michael Leighton

Mrs David Gordon Lennox

Mr Richard Leslie

Mr David L'Estrange

Let's Go Racing

Lets Go Racing I

Mr G.T. Lever

Mr John Lever

Lever, Alexander, Dallas

Lord Leverhulme (H)

Mr A. J. Leveson-Gower

Mrs H. Levy

Lady Lewinton

Mr Colin Lewis

Mr Ben Lewis

Mr Jim Lewis

Mr Keith Lewis

Lewis, Matthews and Pole

Mrs S. Lewis-Harris

Dr Cornel Li

Mr A. Liddiard

Mr Michael Liddy

Mr T. C. Lilburn

Mr Grahame Liles

Mrs Claude Lilley

Mr M.R. Lilley

Mr Luke Lillingston

Mr J-P. Lim

Mrs S. E. Lindley

Mr Nick Littmoden

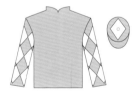

Mrs Emma Littmoden

Mr John Livock

Mr B. J. Llewellyn

Mr D. M. Lloyd

Mr Justin Lloyd

Mr J. W. F. Lloyd-Jones

Lady Lloyd-Webber

Mr A. J. Loader

Mr Keith F. J. Loads

Mr Ian Lochead

Mrs Paul Locke

Mrs Beryl Lockey

Mrs Ann Lockhart

Mrs A. Lockwood

Mrs Lesley Lockwood

Mr D. R. Loder

Sir Edmund Loder

Mrs H. C. Logan

Mr William Lomas

Mrs J. P. Lomax

Mr Neville London

Commander Peter
Longhurst

Countess Of Lonsdale

Mr T. Lonsdale

The Earl Of Lonsdale

Lord Clyde Racing

Lord Daresbury &
J. E. Greenall

Lord Huffington-Smythe
Racing

Lordship Stud

Mrs A. G. Loriston-Clarke

Lostford Manor Stud

Mrs John Loudon

Louisville Syndicate

Mrs A. Lovat

Mr Alan Love

Mrs L. R. Lovell

Mr I. A. Low

Mr D. Lowe   Mr Gary Lowe   C. L. Loyd M. C.   Mr A. Loze   Mr T. P. M. Luard

Mrs R. Luard   Lucayan Stud   Mr Sean Lucey   Mrs E. Lucey-Butler   Mr D. A. Lucie-Smith

Mr Guy Luck   Mr N. E. F. Luck   Mr R. E. Luders-Gibbs   Capt. J. M. G. Lumsden   Mr J. G. Lumsden

Luna Bloodstock   Mrs Kin Lundberg-Young   Miss J. L. Lundgren   Mrs Barbara Lungo   Mr Tony Lusardi

Mrs O. M. Lusty

Mrs W. M. Luttman-Johnson

Mr A. S. Lyburn

Mr Cornelius Lysaght

M. C. S. D. Racing Ltd

M. G. Racing

Mrs B. Macalister

Mr Alvaro Maccioni

Capt J. Macdonald-
Buchanan

Mr A. J. Macdonald-Buchanan

Mr A. R. Macdonald-Buchanan

Mrs A. J. Macdonald-Buchanan

Mrs S. A. Macdonald-Buchanan

Mr Gavin MacEchern

Mr A. G. MacEwan

I. R. K. MacGregor

Miss M.I. MacGregor

Mr J. D. H. Mackenzie

Mr K. C. B. Mackenzie

Mr M. G. Mackenzie

Mrs J. Mackie

Mr J. Macleod

Mr R.M.J. MacNair

Mrs Janis MacPherson

Sir Nevil Macready

Mr B. Mactaggart

Mrs A. H. Mactaggart

Mrs K. B. Mactaggart

Miss K. Magnier (H)

Mrs John Magnier

Mrs John Magnier
(second colours)

Mr Philip Magor

Mr Billy Maguire

Mr Peter Maher

Dr Carla Mahmoud

The Hon Gerald
Maitland-Carew

Mrs Hugh Maitland-Jones

Mr R. G. Makin

Mrs P.J. Makin

Mr Saeed Al Maktoum
Maktoum

Sheikh Ahmed Bin Saeed Al
Maktoum

Mr D. A. Malam

Mr N. Malbon

Mr A. Mallen

Mr Vijay Mallya

Mr Saeed Manana

Mr E. J. Mangan

Mr Charlie Mann

Mr David Mann

Mr G. Mann

Mr I. R. Mann

Mrs C. J. Mann

Mrs J. M. Mann

Mrs M. Mann

Mary, Lady Manton

Lord Manton

Mr Simon Mapletoft

Lady Marchwood

Lord Marchwood

Mrs M. Marfell

Lady Margadale

Exors of the late
Lord Margadale

Mr L. Marinopuolos

Mark Johnston Racing Ltd

Mark Kilner Racing
Syndicates

Mr Richard Marker

Mr D. Marks

Mr Ian Marks

Duke Of Marlborough

Marlborough Racing
Partnership

Mr C. Marner (H)

Mr Barry Marsden

Mr J. L. Marsden

Mr S. P. Marsh

Mrs Henry Marsh

Mrs Jennifer Marsh

Mrs M. K. Marsh

Mr B. C. Marshall

Mr Doug Marshall

Mr K. Marshall

Marston Stud

The Hon Mrs M. A. Marten

Mr C. M. Martin

Mr Gilbert Martin

Mr Glenn Martin

Mr N. Martin

Mrs M. A. Marvin

Mary Reveley Racing Club

Mascalls Stud

Dr Mario Masini

Mr A. J. Mason

Mr A. M. Mason

Mr Paddy Mason

Mr R. G. P. Mason

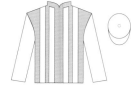

Masons Arms Racing Club

Mr Hadi Masood

Lord Massereene

Mr Vernon Carl Matalon

Mr G.D.P. Materna

Matham Investments

Mrs J. Mathias

Mr F. J. Matthews

Mr F. L. Matthews

Mr R. H. F. Matthews

Mrs S. J. Matthews

Mrs T. S. Matthews

Matthews Breeding and Racing

Mrs Sue Maude

Mr John Maxse

Mrs S. Maxse

Mrs G. C. Maxwell

Mr H. S. May

Mr J. J. May

Mr N. W. E Maynard

Mr P. G. B. Maynard

Mrs Judy Maynard

Mrs J. M. Mayo

Lady Eliza Mays-Smith

Mr B. McAllister

Mr Adrian N. R. McAlpine

Mrs R. McAlpine

Mr K. W. J. McAuliffe

Mr D. McCain

Mrs D. McCain

Mr Harry R. D. McCalmont

Mr Hugh McCalmont

Mr M. R. McCalmont

Mr P. J. McCalmont

Mr Peter V. McCalmont

Mrs Susan McCarthy

Mr C. McCormack

Mrs D. McCormack

McCoy's Neighbours

Mrs G. E. McCrea

Mr R. J. McCreery

Mrs Susan McDonald

Mrs B. A. McEntee

Mrs R. L. McEntee

Mr Colm McEvoy

Miss L. McFadzean

Mrs R. M. McFarlane

Mr B. A. McGarrigle

Mr Luke McGarrigle

Mrs E. McGaughey

Mr T. P. McGovern

Lady McGowan

Mr Jim McGrath

Mr Jack McGrath

Mr Jack McGrath
(second colours)

Mr G. McGuinness

Mr G. M. McGuinness

Mr Ian McInnes

Mr I. W. McInnes

Mrs F. D. McInnes Skinner

Mrs M. McInnes Skinner

Mrs T. J. McInnes Skinner

Mr Willie McKay

Mrs Susie McKeever

Mr W. G. McKenzie-Coles

Mr J. McKinnon

Dr B. I. McLain

Mr Jim McLaren

Mr John McMahon

Mr P. McMahon

Mr Peter McMahon

Mrs J McMahon

Mr J. P. McManus

Mr J. W. McNeill

Mr P. McNeill

Mr Raymond McNeill

Mrs Jill McNeill

Mrs M. McNeill

Mr Stuart McPhee

Mr P. J. McSwiney

Mr Rex L. Mead

Mr Martyn Meade

Mears Group Plc

Meddler Bloodstock

Meddler Racing

Meddler Stud

Mr B. J. Meehan

Mr B. J. Meehan
(second colours)

Mr P. Mellon (H)

Mr Peter Melotti

Mr John Melville

Men Behaving Badly

Miss Janet Menzies

Mr Darren C. Mercer

Mr K. J. Mercer

Mr Stuart M. Mercer

Mr R. Meredith

Mrs Michael Meredith

Mr S. J. Merrick

Merthyr Motor Auctions

Mr A. Merza

Messinger Stud Limited

Mr David T. J. Metcalfe

Miss C. Metcalfe

Mr T. G. Meynell

Sir George Meyrick

Capt Alex Michael

Miss H. Michael

Mr R. P. B. Michaelson

Mr Joe Michell

Midd Shire Racing

Mr G. Middlebrook

Middleham Park Racing

Mr Andy Middleton

Mr B. D. Middleton

Mr Keith Middleton

Mr Nicholas D. Middleton

Mr P. J. Middleton

Mrs K. L. Midgley

Mikado Syndicate

Milbourne Lodge
Partnership

Mr David Milburn

Mr A. Mildmay-White

Mr R. Mildmay-White

Mrs A. Mildmay-White

Mr R. Miles

Mr S.A.M. Milham

Mrs S.J. Milham

Mr Derek Millard

Mrs Bunty Millard

Miss D. Miller

Sir Peter Miller

Miller/Richards Partnership

Mr Robert Miller-Bakewell

Mrs G. Milligan

Mr & Mrs A.G. Milligan

Million In Mind Partnership

Mr B. R. Millman

Major D. N. Mills

Mr A. J. Mills

Mr B. C. Mills

Mr T. G. Mills

Mrs T. G. Mills

Mr Patrick Milmo

Mr A. Milner

Milton Park Stud

Mr Roger Milward

Minster Stud

Mr D. Minton

Mr Barry Minty

Mr J.R. Mitchell

Mr M. Mitchell

Mr M. H. Mitchell

Mr N. R. Mitchell

Mr Philip Mitchell

Mrs D. Mitchell

Mrs Jean Mitchell

Mrs P. B. Mitford-Slades

Mobberley Manor Racing

Mrs Helen Mobley

Mrs Y. Moffatt

Mr A.J. & Mrs A. Moffatt

Sheikh Mohammed

Sheikh Mohammed
(second colours)

Mr T. Mohan

Mollers Racing

Mr C. D. Molony

Mr James Monaghan

Monarch Thoroughbreds

Mr P. Monteith

Miss R. A. Moody

Mr R. C. Moody

Mrs M.E. Moody

Mr G. Moore

Mr R. A. A. Moore

Mr Stan Moore

Mr T.W. Moore

Mrs Susan Moore

Mrs T. Moore

Mr Joe Moran

Mrs Elga Moran

Mr John Morant

Marquesa de Moratalla

Mrs A. S. Mordaunt-Smith

Mr H. R. Morgan

Mr W. G. N. Morgan

Mr Rhydian Morgan-Jones

Mr Michael Moriarty

Mr P. J. Moriarty

Mrs Teresa M. Moriarty

Mr A. Morley

Mrs M. F. D. Morley

Mrs Sylvia Morley

Mr C. P. H. Morlock

Mr P. H. Morris

Mr W. D. Morris

Mr D. Morris

Mr H. F. Morris

Mr Paul Morris

Mrs Hugo Morris

Mr J. Morris

Mr D. Morrison

Mr H. Morrison

Mr M. J. Morrison

Mr A. L. R. Morton

Mr James Morton

Mr C. J. Morton

Mr Brian Moss

Mrs Jill Moss

Mr Derrick Moss

Mr Eddie Moss

Mr H. R. Mould

Mr Russ Mould

Mr J. P. Moulden

Lady Mountain

Miss Debbie Mountain

Sir Denis Mountain

Lord Ivar Mountbatten

Mountgrange Stud

Mr Nabil Mourad

Moyglare Stud Farm

Mrs Sarah Diamandis &
Mrs Celia Woollett

Mrs Thomas Wallis &
Her Family

Mr M. Mulholland

Mr Michael Mullineaux

Mr Seamus Mullins

Mrs Sally Mullins

Mr S. Mulryan

Mr Broderick
Munro-Wilson

Mr W. Murdoch

Mr P. G. Murphy

Mr C.J. Murphy

Mr N.P.C. Musgrave

Lady Rose Musker

Mr W. J. Musson

Mr N. Mustoe

Mr David Myers

Mr Gerald Myers

Mr Martin Myers

Mrs Nicole Myers

Mystic Meg Limited

Mrs David Nagle

Mr D. Napier

Mrs N. Napier

Mr Fawzi Abdulla Nass

National Hunt Partnership

Mr Bill Naylor

Mr D. Naylor

Sir P.V. Naylor-Leyland

Mr Mohamad Razif Nazar

Neardown Stables

Mr B. Neaves

Mr A. E. Needham

Mr J. L. Needham

Mr P. Needham

Mr Terry Neill

Mr H.W. Neilson

Mr M. Nelmes-Crocker

Mr Peter Nelson

Mr W. M. Nelson

Mrs Liz Nelson

Mrs John Nesbitt

Mr C.V. Nesfield

Netherly Racing

Network Training

Mr D. S. Nevison

Newbury Racehorse
Owners Group

Newbyth Stud

Mr A. G. Newcombe

Miss H. M. Newell

Newgate Stud

Newick Park Partnership

Mr D. Newland

Mr J.W. Newman

Mr Nick Newman

NewmarketConnections
.com

Newsells Park Stud

Mr Philip Newton

Mr M. Ng

Mr Michael Ng

Mr Robert Ng

Mr Spyros Niarchos

Mrs Maria I. Niarchos

Mr Philip S. Niarchos

Niarchos Family

Mr Paul Nicholls

Ms Bridget Nicholls

Mr David Nicholson

Mr Keith Nicholson

Mr M. Nicolson

Mr B. E. Nielsen

Nigel & Carolyn Elwes

Mr P. D. Niven

Mr Gerard Nock

Noodles Racing

Norcroft Park Strud

Mr H.G. Norman

Normandie Stud Ltd

North Farm Stud

North West Racing Club

North Lodge Racing Club

Northmore Stud

The Duke of
Northumberland

Northumberland Jumpers

Mr J. Norton

Mr Rex Norton

Mr W. E. Norton

Norton House Racing

Notalotterry

Mr O. Nugent

Sir John Nugent

Mr C.R. Nugent

Mr S. Nunn

Mr C. Y. Nutt

Mr A. E. S. Nuttall

Mr D.A. Nutting

Mrs Y. M. Nye

Oakhill Wood Stud

Lord Oaksey

Oakview Racing

Mr Mohamed Obaida

Lady O'Brien

Mr D. C. O'Brien

Mr K. G. O'Brien

Mr N. J. O'Brien

Mrs V. O'Brien

Mrs N. O'Callaghan

Mr Con O'Connor

Mr D. O'Connor

Mr J. P. M. O'Connor

Mr John O'Connor

Mr W. J. Odell

Mr B. Odner

Sir Robert Ogden C.B.E
LLD

Mrs Andrea O'Grady

Mr Jedd O'Keeffe

Major E. O'Kelly

Mr J. A. B. Old

Mr W. R. Old

Mrs Jim Old

Old Berks Partnership

Old Moss Farm

Old Peartree Stud

Mr G. A. Oldham

Mr M. K. Oldham

Mr A. D. G. Oldrey

Mrs Simon Oldrey

Mrs E. O'Leary

Mrs V. O'Leary

Mr Michael Oliver

Mr N. H. Oliver

Mr P. G. F. Oliver

Mrs Megan Olley

Omni Colour Presentations
Ltd

One In Ten Racing Club

One Stop Partnership

Mrs C. A. O'Neill

Mrs J. G. O'Neill

Mrs Jonjo O'Neill

Only Horses And Fools

Baron F. C. Oppenheim

Mr Peter Oppenheimer

Mrs B. Oppenheimer

Mr A. E. Oppenheimer

Mrs A.E. Oppenheimer

Mrs A. E. Oppenheimer
(second colours)

Mr M.R.C. Opperman

Orange Racing

Orby Racing

Orchard Press

Lady O'Reilly

Sir Anthony O'Reilly (H)

Mr P. J. Orme

Ormonde Racing

Mr & Mrs Sandy Orr

Mr J.A. Osborne

Mr T. E. Osborne

Osborne House Limited

Ossian Construction Ltd

Sir Peter O'Sullevan C.B.E

Miss M. O'Toole

Mr Peter O'Toole

Mr Nicholas O'Toole

Our Friends In The North

Out To Grass Partnership

Miss C. A. Owen

Mr L. R. Owen

Owen Promotions Limited

Mrs H. E. Oxendale

Mr David Oxley

P. F. I. Cole Ltd

Mr W. Packham

Mr Andrew Page

Mrs Gay Page

Mrs David Page

Mr Richard L. Page

Mr Richard Page
(second colours)

Paget Bloodstock

Mr Trevor Painting

The Hon Mrs S. Pakenham

The Hon H. Palmer

Mr J. Palmer-Brown

Mr K. Panos

Mr J. F. Panvert

Mr C. Papaioannou

Park Farm Racing

Park House Partnership

Park Walk Racing (H)

Lady Parker

Lady G. Parker

Sir Eric Parker

Mrs C. Parker Bowles

Brigadier A. H. Parker
Bowles

Mr G. Parkinson

Mrs C.L. Parkinson

Mr M. J. Parr

Mr M Parr

Parr Thoroughbred
Racing I

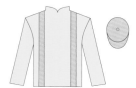

Mr M. Parrish

Mrs R. Parrish

Mr A.R. Parrish

Mr T. J. Parrott

Mr J. C. Parsons

Mr Anthony W. Parsons

Mr J. A. Partridge

Mr Peter Partridge

Mrs J. Parvizi

Mr G. J. Pascoe

Mr Ray Pascoe

Pascoe, G & Brewer, S.

Mr G. Passey

Pat Eddery Racing Limited

Mrs G. M. Paterson

Mr Robin Paterson

Major W. R. Paton-Smith

Mrs Jane Paton-Smith

Patrick Veitch
(Bloodstock a/c)

Mr J. R. Payne

Mr J. S. Payne

Mr Nigel Payne

PCM Racing

Mr Andy Peake

Mr J. L. C. Pearce

Mr Jeff Pearce

Mr Nick Pearce

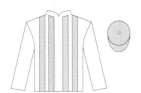

Mrs Lydia Pearce

Miss Helen Pease

Mrs Daphne Pease

Mrs R. Pease

Pegasus Racing Ltd

Mrs E. W. Pegna

Mr A. R. Peirce

Mrs Stella Peirce

Pell-Mell Partners

Mr G. F. Pemberton

Lord Pembroke (H)

The Lord Pender

Pendle Inn Partnership

Mr R. Pennant Jones

Mr Bryan Pennick

Mr Erik Penser

Mrs H. G. Peplinski

Lady Rachel Pepys

Mr R. G. Percival

Mr R. A. H. Perkins

Mr Tony Perkins

Miss L. A. Perratt

Mrs Amanda Perrett

Mr A. P. Perry

Mr A. R. Perry

Mr C. A. G. Perry

Mr Eric Perry

Mrs P. O. Perry

Mrs R. C. Perry

Pertemps Group Limited

Perth Racers

Mr Michael Pescod

Peter Ebdon Racing

Peter J. Douglas
Engineering

Mr G. H. Peter-Hoblyn

Virginia, Lady Petersham

Lord Petersham

Mr N. J. Pewter

Pheasant Inn Partnership

Phil Jen Racing

Phil Lale, Huw Lake

Mrs C. R. Philipson

Mrs N. H. Phillips

Mr Trevor Phillips (H)

Mrs N. Phillips (H)

Mr D. W. Phipps

Mr Hugh Phipps

Mr Ogden Mills Phipps

Mrs S.L. Phipps

Mr E. Pick

Mr J. A. Pickering

Mr J. D. Pickering

Mr J. T. Pickering

Miss Jennifer Pidgeon

Mr L. K. Piggott (H)

Mr B. Pike

Lady Pilkington

Miss S. Pilkington

Mr C. D. Pilkington

Mr M. J. Pilkington

Mrs T. D. Pilkington

Mrs Timothy Pilkington

Sir Thomas Pilkington

Mr G. J. Pinchen

Pinks Gym & Leisure
Wear Ltd

Mr M. C. Pipe

Mr M. Pitman

Mr Richard Pitman

Mrs Elizabeth Pitman

Mr Anthony Pitt

Mr P. J. Pitt

Plantation Stud

Mr David Platt

Mrs S. Platt

Mr P. D. Player

Mrs P. D. Player

Plough Racing

Mr G. W. Plummer

Mrs J. M. Plummer

Plumpton College

Mr O. D. Plunkett

Mrs David Plunkett

Mr Michael Poland

Mrs C. M. Poland

Pompey Racing Club

Mr W. H. Ponsonby

Mr W. H. Ponsonby
(second colours)

Mr Geoffrey Pooley

Mr M. Popham

Lord Porchester

Mr J. A. Porteous

Mrs N. Porter (H)

Mr A. S. B. Portman

Mr J. G. B. Portman

Lord Portsmouth

Mr P. J. D. Pottinger

Mr J. Potts

Mr Jamie Poulton

Mr Julian Poulton

Mrs J. K. Powell

Mrs Mark Powell

Lady D. Powell

Miss Katie Powell

Mr A. J. Powell

Mr G. M. Powell

Mr K. Powell

Mr R. A. Powell

Mr Stuart Powell

Mr Ted Powell

Mr Tim Powell

Mr J. Pownall

Mr John Poynton

Capt A. Pratt

Mr K. A. Pratt

Mrs A. Pratt

Premier Chance Racing

Mrs H. F. Prendergast

Sir Mark Prescott

Mr S. Preston

Mr Anthony Preston

Mr R. Preston

Colonel R.F. Preston (H)

Mr Cecil J. Price

Mr Clive Price

Mr Colin M. Price

Mr A. E. Price

Mr D. F. Price

Mr D. J. Price

Mr G. R. Price

Mr Terry Price

Mrs A. Price

Mrs Dorothy Price

Mr W. E. Prichard

Mr A. W. M. Priestly

Mr R. Prince

Mrs Roy Prince

Mrs J. Pringle

Mr D. R. Pritchard

Mr David Pritchard

Mr J. Pritchard

Mr K. Pritchard

Mr P. A. Pritchard

Mr S. A. Pritchard

Dr P. Pritchard

Mr Stuart Prior

Mr Giles W. Pritchard-
Gordon

Mr Geoffrey Arthur Probin

Mrs Peter Prowting

Mr Jason Puckey

Mr E. Puerari

Mrs Pauline Pullin

Mr John Purcell

Mr A. Purvis

Mr Anthony Pye-Jeary

Qualitair Holdings Ltd

The Queen

Queensberry
Thoroughbreds

Mr D. F. Quinlan

Mrs J. Quinlan

Mr J. M. Quinn

Mr K. J. Quinn

Mr M. Quinn

Mr P. J. Quinn

Mrs Anita Quinn

Mrs S. Quinn

Mr T.K. Quint

R & E H Investments Ltd

R. O. A. Arkle Partnership

Racecourse Medical
Officers Association

Racegoers Club Owners
Group

Raceworld

Racing Club KCB

Racing For Gold

Racing Gifts Ltd

Racing Ladies

Racing Thoroughbreds Plc

Capt C. Radclyffe

Mrs C. Radclyffe (L)

Radlett Racing

Mrs M. A. Rae Smith

Raglan Racing Club

Rags to Riches

Mr B. Rai

Mrs J. D. Railton

H. H. Princess Premila
of Rajpipla

Rams Racing Club

Major General C.A.
Ramsay

Miss E. L. Ramsden

Mr Jonathan Ramsden

Mrs J. R. Ramsden

Mrs Sheila Ramsden

Lord Ranfurly (H)

Mr Christopher Ransom

Ali Bul Rashid

Mr Christopher P. Ranson

Mr Mohammed Rashid

Miss K. Rausing

The Rt Hon The Baroness
Rawlings

Mr A. C. Raymond

Mr T. W. Raymond

Mr R. Rayner

Mrs O. Razzini

RDM Racing

Mr J.A. Rea

Mrs D. M. Read

Mrs Julie Read

Read O'Gorman Racing

Realistic Racing

Mr Frank Reay

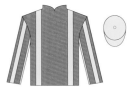

Mrs M. D. Rebori

Red Alert Racing

Redcroft Racing

Redenham Racing Group

Mr Des Redhead

Mrs P. Reditt

Mr Harry Redknapp

Ms Linda Redmond

Mr D. Redvers

Miss Juliet E. Reed

Mr J. E. Reed

Mr W. J. Reed

Mrs Elizabeth Reed

Mr Guy Reed

Mr N. Reed Herbert

Mr C. Reeder-Thomas

Mr D. Rees

Mr D. A. Rees

Mr Steven Rees

Mrs G. S. Rees

Mrs H. E. Rees

Mr J. F. Reeves

Mrs C. C. Regalado-
Gonzalez

Mr G. Regan

Mr J. Regan

Mr A. S. Reid

Mrs E. Reid

Mrs A. Reid Scott

Mrs Fiona Reilly

Reliance Car Hire
Services Ltd

Mrs J. Renfree-Barons

Mr D. C. Renton

Lady Renwick

Mr Dick Renwick

Mr K. G. Reveley

Mrs M. Reveley

Mrs R. H. Reynolds

Mrs Y. J. Reynolds

Mr J.P.L. Reynolds

Mr T. M. B. Rice

Mr P. M. Rich

Richard Cook Ltd

Richard Green
(Fine Paintings)

Mrs C. M. Richard OBE

Mr D. J. B. Richards

Mr D. M. Richards

Mr D. R. Richards

Mr J. B. J Richards

Mr T. J. Richards

Mr A.J. Richards

Mr A.J. Richards
(second colours)

Mr C. N. Richardson

Mrs S. L. Richardson

The Duke of Richmond
& Gordon

Mr J. H. Richmond-Watson

Mrs B. J. Richmond-Watson

Mrs R. N. Richmond-
Watson

Mr S.J. Richmond-Watson

Mr R.T. Ricketts

Mr E. Rider

Ridge Racing

Ridgeway Downs Racing

Ridgeway Farm Racing

Ridgewood Racing

Dr Ali Ridha

Mrs D. Ridley

Mr S. H. Riley

Mr T. S. M. S. Riley-Smith

Mr Mark Rimell

Mrs M. R. T. Rimell

Mrs Mercy Rimell

Mr E. B. Rimmer

Mr D. S. Ringer

Mr M. W. E. Ritchie-Noakes

Riverdance Consortium

Mr Henry Rix

ROA Arkle Partnership

Mr C. G. Roach

Miss H. S. Robarts

Mr Ben Robarts

Mrs G. A. Robarts

Mr D. M. Robb

Sir John Robb

Mr E. M. G. Roberts

Mr Gary Roberts

Mr Mike Roberts

Mr Raymond Roberts

Mrs N. J. Roberts

Mrs E. Roberts

Mr David Roberts

Mr S. H. Robertshaw

Mrs K. Roberts-Hindle

Mr Sanford R. Robertson

Mr Nick Robey

Mr M. W. Robins

Mrs L. J. Robins

Major G. M. Robinson

Mr A. L. Robinson

Mr A. W. Robinson

Mr D. C. Robinson

Mr D. M. Robinson

Mr Graham Robinson

Mr J. B. Robinson

Lady Roborough

Lord Roborough

Mr G. Robotti

Mr John Robson

Mr Paul Robson

Rockfel Thoroughbreds

Mr Graeme Roe

Roemex Ltd

Mr A. Rogers

Mr Anthony Rogers

Mrs Sonia Rogers

Dr Klaus E. Rohde

Roldvale Limited

Mr M. R. Rollett

Mr W. M. Rollett

Mr E. Rollinson

Lord Ronaldshay

Mrs J. Roncoroni

Mr T. D. Rootes

Mr Roland Roper

Mr Steven Roper

Mr Pedro Rosas

Roseberry Racing

Mr Harvey Rosenblatt

Mr Warren Rosenthal

Mr Campbell Ross

Lord Rotherwick

Lady Rothschild

Rowan Stud Partnership

Mr Richard Rowe

Mrs G. Rowland-Clark

Duke of Roxburghe

Mrs Susan Roy

Royal Ascot Racing Club

Mrs Michael Royds

Mr S. Rudolf

Runs In The Family

Mr Martin Rushton

Miss V. A. Russell

Mr D. I. Russell

Mr Con Rutledge

Dr T. A. Ryan

Mr Cathal M. Ryan

Mr E. P. Ryan

Mr James Ryan

Mr M.A. Ryan

Mr Oliver Ryan

Mr P. C. Ryan

Mr Simon Ryan

Miss S.A Ryder

Ryder Racing Ltd

Mr A. Sadik

Mr Ali Saeed

Mr Wafic Said

The Hon Simon Sainsbury

Mr Hilal Salem

Mr Faisal Salman

Mrs D. Salmon

Mrs Linda Salter

Salter, Wilson & Oakes

Mr Omar Samaha

Miss Mary Samworth

Miss S.L. Samworth

Mrs D.C. Samworth

Sand Associates

Mr W.F. Sandercock

Miss Brooke Sanders

Mr Gavin Sanders

Mr P.J. Sanderson

˙Sandicroft Stud I

Mrs P.J. Sands

Mrs B. Sands

Mr R.P. Sandys-Clarke

Mr A. Sangster

Mr B.V. Sangster

Mrs B.V. Sangster

Mr G.E. Sangster

Sangster Family

Mr A.D. Sansome

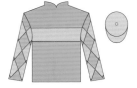

Mr Richard Santulli

Saracen Racing

Prince Abdul Aziz Bin Saud

Prince Torki M. Saud

Mr P.W. Saunders

Mrs J.A. Saunders

Mr P.D. Savill

Mrs A. Savill

Mr Joss Saville

Mrs Dianne Sayer

Mr M.A. Scaife

Mr Gerry Scanlon

Mr T.A. Scaramanga

Lord Scarborough (H)

Scart Stud

Mr Urs E. Schwarzenbach

Mrs Francesca
Schwarzenbach

Miss H.C. Scorah

Mr A.S. Scott

Mr D.I. Scott

Mr Pierpont Scott

Mr W.A. Scott

Mrs E.B. Scott

Sir Anthony Scott

Sir James Scott

Scott Hardy Partnership

Mr P.J. Scott Plummer

Mrs V. Scott Watson

Mrs H. Scott-Barrett

Mr Hugh Scott-Barrett

Mrs P. Scott-Dunn

Mrs A.W. Scott-Harden

Mr James Scrimgeour

Miss A.M.M. Scrope

Miss H.C. Scrope

Mr R.H. Scrope

Mrs S.E. Scrope

Mr M. Scudamore

Mrs Marilyn Scudamore

Scuderia Archi Romani

Scuderia Briantea SRL

Scuderia Golden Horse SRL

Scuderia Rencati Srl

Mr Robin F. Scully

Mr N.S. Seddon-Brown

Seddon-Brown Partnership

Mrs M. Segal

Mr Gary Seidler

Mr J. Selby

Miss J. Semple

Senate Racing Partnership

Mr Yusof Sepiuddin

Mr John Seth-Smith

Mr Brian Seward

Miss N.G. Sexton

Mr C.J. Sexton

Seymour Bloodstock (UK) Ltd

Mr Ahmed Al Shafar

Lord Shaftesbury

HRH Sultan Ahmad Shah

Ahmed Ali Shaiba

Mrs Paul Shanahan

Mr C.C. Shand Kydd

Mr W. Shand Kydd

Mrs William Shand Kydd

Shangri-La Racing Club

Mr Christopher Shankland

Mr Hugh J. Shapter

Mr Robin Sharp

Major D. C. B. Shaw

Mr D.W. Shaw

Mr James Shaw

Mr John Sheehan

Mrs Eileen Sheehan

Mrs P. J. Sheen

Shefford Valley Stud

Mrs Ying Shen

Mr Liam Sheridan

Mr C.E. Sherry

Mrs P. Sherwood

The Hon Mrs S. Sherwood

Mrs K.P. Sherwood

Mr C. Shiacolas

Mr Nigel Shields

Mr M. Shirley

Mrs E.M. Shirley-Beaven

Mr T.E. Short

Shortgrove Manor Stud

Miss L.C. Siddall

Sir David Sieff

Mr Jules Sigler

Mrs Heather Silk

Prof D.B.A. Silk

Mr Andrew Sim

Mr Andrew Sim
(second colours)

Simon Mapletoft Racing

Mr J. D. Simpson-Daniel

Mr John E. Sims

Mr M. Sines

Mr Joe Singh

Sir Peter And
Lady Gibbings

Mrs R. J. Skan

Skara Glen Stables

Skeltools Ltd

Mr Dennis Skinner

Mr R. C. Skinner

Mrs B. Skinner

Mrs M. E. Slade

Mr D. Slingsby

Mr Peter Slip

Mr John Smart

Mr Andy J. Smith

Mr Bob W. Smith

Mr Clive D. Smith

Mr Edmund Smith

Mr Ian Smith

Mr J. C. Smith

Mr Julian Smith

Mr Neil Smith

Mr Terry E. G. Smith

Mr H. Stephen Smith

Dr Michael Smurfit

Mr J. Snook

Sir M. Sobell (H)

Mr A. N. Solomons

Mr Humphrey Solomons

Solway Stayers

Lady Somerleyton

Lord Somerleyton

Mr Arthur Souch

Southern Bloodstock

Mr John Southway

Mr R.J.O. Sowerby

Mr M. E. Sowersby

Ms Ellen R. Sowle

Mr Alan Sowle

Mr Eamon Spain

Mr G.H. Sparkes

Mr A. K. Sparks

Miss R. M. Spearing

Mr J. Spearing

Speedlith Group

Mr Anthony Speelman

Mr A. D. Spence

Mr J. Spence

Mr Howard Spooner

Mr Christopher Sporborg

Sporting Occasions

sportsdays.co.uk

Mr N. R. A. Springer

Springs Equestrian
Partnership

St Gatien Racing Club

Mr M. G. St Quinton

Mr Graham Stacey

Stag And Huntsman

Mr Louis Stalder

Stall Capricorn

Stamford Bridge
Partnership

The Hon Mrs Stanley

The Hon Peter Stanley

Mr Tony Staple

Star Alliance and K. Reveley

Steadshaw Partnership

Steadshaw Partnership 2

Mr Frank Stella

Mr Allan Stennett

Mr G. Stephenson

Mr I. H. Stephenson

Mr J. Stephenson

Ms R. Z. Stephenson

Mr P.J. Stephenson

Sterling Racing Syndicate

Mr C. H. Stevens

Mr G. C. Stevens

Mr Guy Stevenson

Mr J. Stevenson

Mr B. T. Stewart-Brown

Mrs M. Stirk

Miss N. Stirling

Mr J. E. Stockton

Mr D. R. Stoddart

Mr Michael Stoddart

Ms Caron Stokell

Stonethorn Stud Farms Ltd

Ms Christina Storey

Sir Michael Stoute

Major I. C. Straker

Mr L. Straszewski

Mrs Derek Strauss

Mr George
Strawbridge (H)

Stretton Racing

Mr D. Stronach

Mrs Bernice Stronge

Mr H. A. B. Stroud

Miss Charlotte C. Stucley

Miss T. Sturgis

Mr R. T. Sturgis

Mr W. E. Sturt

Lady Stuttaford

Mr Saeed Suhail

Mr Salem Suhail

Mr Khalifa Sultan

Mr C. W. Sumner

Mr J. B. Sumner

Mrs B. Sumner

Mr John B. Sunley

Sunpak Potatoes

Supreme Corner Gang

Supreme Team

Surf N'Turf Racing

Sussex Racing

Mr D. D. Sutherland

Evelyn, Duchess of Sutherland

Bernard Swain

Mr David Swan

Mr P. Sweeting

Mr Rupert Sweeting

Swift Racing

Mr R. J. Swinbourne

Mr J. A. Swinburne

Mr Roy Swinburne

Mr J. Swinnerton

Miss B. Swire

Mrs C. A. T. Swire

Miss A. H. Sykes

Mr David Sykes

Mr Walt Sylvester

Mr Lee M. Symes

Syndicate 2001

Syndicate 2002

T. Wallace & Partners

Mr M. Tabor

Lady Juliet Tadgell

Mr Gary A. Tanaka

Mr T Taniguchi

Miss E. J. Tanner

Tantivy Racing Partnership

Mr T. P. Tate

Mrs L. C. Taylor

Team Havana

Team Valor

Mr P. T. Tellwright

Mr W. Tellwright

Lady Tennant

Mr George E. K. Teo

Teviot Stud

Terrible Business
Partnership

The Adventure Partnership

The Beare Family

The Behrajan Partnership

The Blanford Partnership

The Boardroom Syndicate

The Bond Girls Partnership

The Caledonian Racing
Society

The Chantilly Partnership

The Christie Partnership

The Comic Strip
Heroes Too

The Country Side

The Courters

The Crail Partnership

The Friar Tuck Racing Club

The Galloping Punters

The Gap Partnership

The Haut de Gamme Partnership

The Hilton Seven

The Hole In The Wall Gang

The Hopeful Partnership

The Knavesmire Partnership

The Links Partnership

The Living Legend Racing Partnership

The Lucky 5 Partnership

The National Stud

The National Stud Owner-Breeders' Club

The Poppet Partnership

The Queen Mother (H)

The Maybe Syndicate

T.H.E. Racing

The Racing Guild

The Red Shirt Brigade Racing Club

The Ridgeway Partnership

The Royal Ascot Racing Club

The Stablemates

The Stan James Winners

The Stay Positive Partnership

The Three Amigos

The Waney Racing Group

The Web Partnership

The Winning Line

Theobalds Stud

Mr & Mrs R.J. Thomas

Mr W. Ralph Thomas

Mr Iwan Thomas

Mr M.A. Thomas

Mr A.A. Thomason

Lady Thompson

Mr D. Thompson

Mr David Thompson

Mr Erik Thorbek

Thornaby Racing Club

Mr C. W. Thornton

Thoroughbred Farms Ltd

Thurloe Finsbury

Thurloe Thoroughbreds

Mr R.G. Thurston

Mrs Richard Tice

Mr J. D. N. Tillyard

Times Of Wigan

Mr S. P. Tindall

Tipp-Ex Rapid Racing

Mr C. L. Tizzard

Mr G. Tong

Mr Raymond Tooth

Lady Sophia Topley

Mrs V. A. Tory

Mr K. Tork

The Hon Mrs Townshend

Mr Paul Townsley

Treble Chance Partnership

Mr M.P.N. Tregoning

Trillium Place Racing

Mr John M. Troy

Mr S. L. Tse

Mr J. C. Tuck

Mr M. J. Tuckey

Mrs D. S. Tuke

Miss Catherine Tuke

Mr Freddie Tulloch

Turf 2000 Limited

Mr Ambrose Turnbull

Mr Frank Turner

Mr J. M. Turner

Tweenhills Racing Ltd

Mr N. A. Twiston-Davies

Mr Audley Twiston-Davies

Mr Eddie Tynan

Mr James Unett

Mrs A. M. Upsdell

Mr M. D. I. Usher

Usk Valley Stud

Mr Chris van Hoorn

Mr E. Vaux

Mrs F. A. Veasey

Lady Vestey

Lord Vestey

Mrs R. A. C. Vigors

Mr R. C. C. Villers

Dr C. Vittadini (H)

Mr B. H. Voak

Recke C. Von Der

Mr J. S. Wainwright

Mrs U. Wainwright

Mr Robert Waley-Cohen

Mrs Linda Walker

Mrs S. Wall

Mr M. J. Wallace

Mr J. R. Wallis

Mrs Jane Walter

Mrs K. Walton

Mr M. H. Walton

Mr P. T. Walwyn

Mr George Ward

Mrs C. J. Ward

Mrs C. A. Warden

Mr M. Ward-Thomas

Mr Terry Warner

Lady Carolyn Warren

Lady Carolyn Warren
(second colours)

Mr L. A. Warren

Warwick Racecourse
Owners Club

Mr J. B. Waterfall

Waterline Racing Club

Lady Wates

Lady G. Wates

Mr A. T. A. Wates

Mr M. E. Wates

Sir Christopher Wates

Major E. J. Watt

Mr Michael H. Watt

Mr Robbie Watt

Mr W. S. Watt

Lady Katharine Watt

Mr Adam Waugh

Wavertree Racing Club (2002) Ltd

Mr J. R. Weatherby

R. I. Webb-Bowen

Mr Paul Webber

Mrs John Webber

Wedgewood Estates

Mr Jim Weeden

Mr Colin Weedon

Mr Ed Weetman

Mrs Elizabeth Weinfeld

Exors of the late Lord Weinstock

Mrs John M. Weld

Lady Richard Wellesley

Mr Mark Wellings

Mr L. Wells

Mr H. Wellstead

Mr A. M. Welstead (H)

Wendals Herbs Ltd

Wentworth Racing (Pty) Ltd

Sir Neil Westbrook

Duke of Westminster

Anne, Duchess of Westminster (H)

Mr Lee Westwood

Mr J. Weymes

Lady Whent

Mr D. W. Whillans

Mr D. W. Whillans (second colours)

Mr J. G. White

Mrs G. F. White

Mrs C. White

Mr R. John White

Whitesmith Farm Stud

Mr W. T. Whittle

Mr James Wigan

Mrs Dare Wigan

Mrs James Wigan

Mr Cecil Wiggins

Mr I. A. N. Wight

Mr J. P. H. Wight

Mr W. G. R. Wightman

Mr P. J. H. Wills

Wild Beef Racing

Mr Chris Wilkinson

Miss V. M. Williams

Mr D. L. Williams

Mr Ian Williams

Mr O. J. Williams

Mr Paul Williams

Mr S. J. Williams

Mr Stuart C. Williams

Mr A. N. Williamson

Mrs Jenny Willment

Mr Alan Willoughby

Mr Guy Willoughby

Dr Catherine Wills

Mr John Wills

Willsford Racing
Incorporated

Mr F. C. T. Wilson

Mr G. Wilson

Mr George Wilson

Mr Noel Wilson

Mr T. W. Wilson

Mr Tom Wilson

Mr W. R. Wilson

Mrs N. C. Wilson

Mrs Caroline Wilson

Mrs E. W. Wilson

Major R. G. Wilson

Mrs R. M. Wilson

Win-A-Lot Syndicate

Mr A. Winchester

Windflower Overseas
Holdings Inc

Windsor House
Thoroughbreds

Mr P. Winkworth

Winning Post Limited

Winterbeck Manor Stud

Winterfields Farm Ltd

Mr D. J. Wintle

Mr P. Wolfson

Mr Ronnie Wood

Mrs A. L. Wood

Mrs A. R. Wood

Wood Hall Stud Limited

Mr J. E. Wood

Woodcote Stud Ltd

Woodford Valley Racing

Woodhaven Racing

Mr L. T. Woodhouse

Mr R. D. E. Woodhouse

Mr David G. Woods

Mr S. Woods

Mrs Joanne Woods

Mr G. Woodward

Mr R. M. Woollacott

Woolpack Farm
Partnership

Mrs J. S. Wootton

Mr B. M. Wootton

Mr M. Worcester

Mrs Emma Worrell

Mrs M. A. Worsdell

Mrs Georgina Worsley

WRB Racing Syndicates

Mr Alan A. Wright

Mr Christopher Wright

Mr John Wade

WWW.Clarendon Racing.
Com

www.mark-kilner-racing.
com

Major M. G. Wyatt

Mr C. G. P. Wyatt

Wyck Hall Stud

Mr Graham Wylie

Mr M. Wynne-Jones

Mr J. A. Wynn-Williams

Wyvern Racing

Miss A. J. Yardley

Mr Dennis Yardy

Yarm Racing Partnership

Yarm Skip Alliance

Mr David Yarrow

Mr J Yates

Mr D. N. Yeadon

Mrs Anne Yearley

Yellow River Partnership

Mr Albert Yemm

Yeo Racing Partnership

Yeoman Homes Limited

Mrs Jean F.P. Yeomans

Yes-No-Wait…Sorries

Mr N. S. Yong

Col E. C. York

Mr R. H. York

Mr S. D. York

Mrs E.C. York

York City Soccer Club

Yorkshire Lancashire Alliance (H)

Yorkshire Point-To-Point Club

Yorkshire Racing & Derek Blackhurst

Yorkshire Racing Club Owners Group

Mr Teruya Yoshida

You Boyz Is Lost

You Can Be Sure

Mr E. Young

Mrs A. M. Young

Major J.C.K. Young

Mr David C. Young

Mr E. J. G. Young

Mr John Young

Mrs A.M. Young

Mrs Laura J. Young

Young Guns Syndicate

You're Having A Laugh
Racing Club

Mr Theo Zachariades

Zak Facta Ltd

Mr David Zeffman

Mr Perry H. Zellick

Zen Racing

Zero 3 Racing

Zero's To Hero's

Lord Zetland

Mr Paul Zetter

Mrs Carrie Zetter-Wells

Mrs L. Ziegler

Zubieta Limited

Zycko Ltd

1st Regiment Royal Horse
Artillery (H)

1st The Queens Dragoon
Guards

14th Regiment Royal
Artillery

40th Regiment Royal
Artillery (H)

47th Regiment Royal
Artillery (H)

100th (Yeomanry)
Regiment RA (V) (H)

2nd Carlton Partnership

18 Red Lions Partnership

21st Century Racing

1966 World Cup Winners
Sporting Club (H)

Tank Française *Cartier*

2003 *Cartier* Award Winners

Cartier Two-Year-Old Colt: One Cool Cat (USA)
Arnaud Bamberger, Managing Director of Cartier UK presents
the award to Tom Magnier representing his mother.

Cartier Three-Year-Old Colt: Dalakhani (IRE)
Princess Zahra Aga Khan on behalf of her father.

The Daily Telegraph Award of Merit: John Oaksey

Lord Oaksey, founder of the IJF receives his award from The Hon Jeremy Deedes.

Cartier Older Horse: Falbrav (IRE)

Luciano Salice receives the award on behalf of owners Scuderia Rencanti Srl and Teruya Yoshida.

Cartier Stayer: **Persian Punch (IRE)**

Owner Jeff Smith received the loudest applause on behalf of his evergreen stayer.

Cartier Two-Year-Old Filly: **Attraction (GB)**

The Duke of Roxburghe accepts the award for his multiple Group 1 winning filly.

Cartier Three-Year-Old Filly: **Russian Rhythm (USA)**

Patricia and David Thompson of Cheveley Park Stud.

Cartier Sprinter: **Oasis Dream (GB)**
Owner Khalid Abdullah's Racing Manager Teddy Grimthorpe

Cartier Horse of the Year: **Dalakhani (IRE)**
Princess Zahra Aga Khan with Trainer Alain Royer-Dupre

Index

Brunton Sir Gordon
Bryant Mrs M. O.
Bryant Mr M.
Bryce Mr Colin
Bryce Mrs Melba
Buckfield Mr P.R.
Buckingham Thoroughbreds
Buckley Mr C.C.
Buckley Mr M. A.
Buckley Mr Michael
Buckley Sir Roger
Buckram Oak Holdings
Budge Mr A. F. **36**
Budge Mrs A. F.
Budgett Mr A. M.
Budgett Mr C. M.
Builders Bobby
Buller Mr A. W.
Bullimore Mr Simon
Bulwer Long Mrs W. H.
Bulwer-Long Capt. T.
Bunter Mr Nigel
Burdett Mr P.
Burgess Mr D.
Burgess Mr R.
Burgoyne Mr A. P.
Burke Mr D. J.
Burke Mrs Valda
Burke Mr B.R.
Burley Appliances Ltd
Burlington, The Earl Of The Earl Of
Burne Captain Francis
Burnet Mrs L.
Burnham Lady
Burns Mrs Seamus
Burns Mr William
Burrell Mr A.
Burrell Mrs Ann
Burrell Mrs Mark
Burridge Mr R.
Burridge Mr R. C.
Burrough Miss M. D.
Burrough Mr B. R. H. **37**
Burton Agnes Bloodstock
Bury Lady Mairi
Bush Mr J. H. C.
Bush Mr N.
Bush Syndicate
Bute, Executors of The Late Dowager Lady
Butler Mr David M.
Butler Mr Ron
Butt Bt Sir Kenneth
Butt Bt Mr W. J.
Butter Lady
Butterfield Mr T.
Butterworth Mrs B
Buxton Mr A.
Bycroft Mr N. M.
Byculla Thoroughbreds
Byrne Mr A. J.
Byrne Mr David
Byrne Miss Gillian
Byron-Scott Mr R.

C

C.R. Marks (Banbury) **37**
Caborn-Waterfield Mr M.

Cabrera-Vargas Mr R.
Cadbury Mr Peter
Cadogan The Earl
Cadogan (second colours) The Earl **38**
Cadwaladr Mrs C. J.
Caerphilly Building Supplies Ltd
Cahill Mr Bill
Cairns Mr J. A. F.
Caldwell Mr T. H.
Caley Mr W. L.
Callaghan Mr A.
Callaghan Mrs J.
Callaghan Miss M. F.
Callow Mr J. D.
Callow Mr James
Callow Mr S.
Calver Mrs C.
Calvert Carpets
Calvert Mr M.
Calypso Racing
Camacho Miss Julie
Camacho Mrs S.
Cambell Lt-Col Colin
Cambidge Mr B. R.
Cambidge Mrs T. A.
Cameron The Hon Mrs C.
Cameron Mr Ian
Cameron Mr Robbie
Cameron Mr W. O. H.
Cameron-Rose Mrs H. A.
Campbell Mr J. W. D.
Campbell Fraser Mrs Patrick
Campbell The Hon Mrs Nicole
Campbell Golding Mr C. C. **39**
Campbell-Andenaes Mrs Mette
Campbell-Harris Mrs Zara
Campion Mr A. M.
Candy Mr Henry
Candy Mrs Henry
Cann Mr Brian
Canisbay Bloodstock
Cantillon Mr Don
Cantillon Mrs Edward
Cantle Mr Brian D.
Cantoni Mr R.
Cantrill Mr John
Capricorn Hospitality
Car Colston Hall Stud
Carbery Mr K.
Cardiff Mrs R. D.
Carew Pole Sir Richard
Carey Mr D. N.
Carlini Cozzi Dr Ornella
Carlson Mrs L. W.
Carlyle Mr J. M.
Caroe Miss C. J. E.
Carr Mr Ashley
Carr Mr C. D.
Carr Mr David
Carr Mr J. M.
Carr Mr P. J.
Carr-Evans Mrs J.
Carrington Mrs B. J.
Carroll Mr Seamus **40**
Carsberg Mrs S.
Carson Mr R.M.
Carson Mr W.H.
Carstairs Mr G.
Carter Lady Celina
Cartmell Mr P.

Cartridge Mr P.T.
Carvill Mr R. K.
Case Mr B. I.
Case Mrs N. K.
Case Racing Partnership
Cash Mrs J.
Cashman Mr L.
Casino Racing Partnership
Caslon Mr D. H.
Casolari Mr Alberto
Cassidy Miss Nuala
Cassidy Mr T
Castle Mr J. M.
Castlemead Developments Limited
Castlemore Securities Limited
Castles UK
Cathcart Countess
Catherwood Mr H. R. C.
Catherwood Mrs Stewart
Cathorne (H) Lord
Caudwell Mr W. F.
Caulfield Mr Mike
Cavendish Lord
Cavendish Racing **41**
Cawley Mrs Christine
Cawood Mr N.
Cazalet (H) Sir Peter
Cazenove Mr G.
Cazenove Clear Heights (H)
Cecil (H) Mr H. R. A.
Cecil Mrs J
Cecil Mrs Vanessa
Cedar Lodge 2000 Syndicate
Celtic Racing
Centaur Racing Ltd
Cereal Partners
Chaddleworth Partnership
Chalfont Foodhalls Ltd
Challen Miss J. A.
Challis Miss Louise
Chamberlain Mr A. J.
Chamberlain Mr N.
Chamberlain Mr T.
Chamberlayne Mr E. C.
Chamberlayne Mr M. E.
Chambers Mr G.
Chambers Mrs Peter
Chamings Mr P. R.
Champion Mr B. J.
Champion Mr Fred
Champion Mr R. W.
Champneys Partnership
Chance Mrs M.
Chance Prof. E. M. **42**
Chandler Mrs S. S.
Chandris Mrs Alexandra J.
Chang Dr Fuk To
Channon Mr M.
Chapman Mr David W.
Chapman Mr F. W. W.
Chappell Major D. N.
Chappell Mr N.T.
Chappell Mr T. G. A.
Chapple Mr J. F. R.
Chapple-Hyam Mrs Jane
Charalambous Mr P.
Charge Mr Maurice
Charles-Jones Mr G. F. H.
Charles-Jones Mrs Jessica
Charlesworth Mr D.

Charlock Stud
Charlton Mr A.
Charlton Mr Harry
Charnock Bates
Charsam Limited
Charter Mr Peter
Charterhouse Holdings Plc
Chartwell Racing
Chasetown Civil Engineering Ltd
Chaworth-Musters Mrs M.V.
Chelgate Public Relations Ltd
Chell Mr Christopher
Chelsea Lady
Chelsea Artisans Ltd **43**
Cheltenham Race Club Owners Group
Cheltenham Racing Ltd
Chemipetro Limited
Chenery Mrs J. A.
Cheshire Mr Layton T.
Chester Mr J. R.
Chesters (H) Mr Patrick
Chetwode Lord
Cheveley Park Stud
Chevington Stud
Cheyne Mr J. R.
Chiang Mr T. C.
Chick Mr Timothy N.
Chicken Mr Brian
Chisenale-Marsh Mr H. A.
Choake Ms J.
Cholmeley Lady
Chong Mr G.W.
Chown Mrs Susie
Chris & Antonia Deuters
Christodoulou Mr Athos
Christopher Mr D.J.
Christy Partnership
Chung Mrs E.
Chung Mr G. C. H.
Chung Mr H. C.
Church Miss Vanessa
Churchills Ltd
Churston Mr D. G.
Churton Capt. D. N.V. **44**
Churton Mrs Geoffrey
Circular Distributors Ltd
City Industrial Supplies Ltd
City Racing Club
Clague Mr J. D.
Clague Lady
Claisse Mr S. J.
Clanwilliam (H) Lady
Clapham Mr D. J.
Clapperton Mr A. W. F.
Clare Mr W. M.
Clarendon Thoroughbred Racing
Claret & Blue Army
Clark Mr G. N.
Clark Mr J. C.
Clark Mr J. W. P.
Clark Mr M. A.
Clark Mr Martin W.
Clark Mr N. C.
Clark Mr Philip E.
Clark Mr R. J.
Clark Mr Simon N.
Clark Mr W. D.
Clarke Lady
Clarke Mr A.
Clarke Mr C. C.

Clarke Mr Derek
Clarke Mr M. J.
Clarke Mr Roger
Clarke Mr S. R. **45**
Clarke Mr Simon W.
Clarke Mr T.
Clarke Mrs C. A.
Clarke Mrs C. M.
Clarke Mrs E. M.
Clarke (H) Sir Stanley
Clarkson Mr Geoffrey
Classic Gold
Clay Mr Robert N.
Clay Mr W.
Clayton Mr C.
Clayton Mr D. G.
Clayton Mr J. A.
Clayton Mrs M. A.
Clear Racing
Clee Mr Derek D.
Clegg Mrs Sylvia
Clement Mrs C.
Clements Mr I. R.
Clements Mr James
Cleveley Mrs L.
Cleveley Mr P. J.
Cliff Mr A. D.
Cliff Mr David
Clifford Mr Brian
Clifford Mrs Irene
Clifton-Brown Mr R. L.
Clinton Mr P. L.
Clinton Lord
Clipper Group Holdings **46**
Cliveden Stud
Clough Mr E. R.
Clowes Mr H. B. B.
Clowes Mr Tim
Clubb Mr M. J. G.
Clutton Mr Nigel
Clutton Lady Sarah
Coach House Racing
Coates Mr D. S.
Coates Mr Michael
Coburn Mr Mick
Cochrane The Hon Thomas
Cochrane Of Cults Lord
Cockburn Mr A. D.
Cockerell Mr Barry J.
Cockerill Mr B.
Cocks Mr David
Cody Dr Frederick W.J.
Cody-Boutcher Mr R. B.
Coghlan-Everitt Mrs J.
Cohen Mr Andrew L.
Cohen Mr L.
Cohen Mr Richard J.
Cohn (H) Mr Seymour
Coker Mr K. A.
Coldrey Capt. Christopher
Cole Mr John
Cole Mr P. F. I.
Cole Mrs P. F. I.
Coleing Mr A. J. **47**
Coleman Mr K. F.
Coley Mr A. R.
Colfax Window Systems Ltd
Colin Brown Racing II
Colin Davey Racing
Coller Miss E. M. L.
Collett Mr Brian

Collier Miss Jane
Colling Mr James E.S.
Collingridge Mr H. J.
Collingwood Mr E. E.
Collingwood-Cameron Mrs E. S. M.
Collins Mr A. K.
Collins Mr B. J.
Collins Mr Ben
Collins Mr J. E. H.
Collins Mr K. E.
Collins Mr Lincoln
Collins Mr Ron
Collins Mr T.
Collins Mr T. H.
Collins Mr Tim
Collins Lady
Collinson Mr C.I.
Collinson Mrs Isabel M.
Colquhoun Mr Alex
Colquhoun Mr C. F.
Coltman Mr Davis
Colver Miss Elizabeth
Colvin Mr S. E. **48**
Compton Mr A. P.N
Compton Mr Stuart E.
Concertina Racing
Conkwell Grange Stud Ltd
Connaught Racing
Connell Mr J. E.
Connell Sir Michael
Connell Lady
Connolly Mr J. M.
Connop Miss B. J.
Connor Mr John
Conroy Mrs Jacqueline
Constable Mr D. P.
Constant Mr S.
Conway Mr A. J.
Conway Mrs J.
Conway Mrs Thomas
Cook Mr A. J.
Cook Mr M. R. M.
Cook Mrs Pippa
Cook Mr R.
Cook Mr Robert E.
Cookson Mr C. J.
Cookson Mrs M. J. B.
Coombe Wood Racing Syndicate
Coombs Mrs J.
Cooper Mr Brian
Cooper Mr C. W.
Cooper Mr D. C. G.
Cooper Mr D. S. **49**
Cooper Mrs Diane Christine
Cooper Mr G. I.
Cooper Mr G.V.
Cooper Mr Nicholas
Cooper Mr P. D.
Cooper Mr P. E.
Cooper Mrs Sarah
Cooper Sir Richard
Cooper Mr Robert
Cope Mrs D.
Cope Miss H.L.
Copley Mr Anthony D.
Corbett The Hon Mrs J. M.
Corbett Mr M.
Corbett Mr P. J.
Corbett Mr R. A. C.
Corby Mr Tim
Cordingley Mr Simon

Coriolan Links Partnership
Coriolis Partnership
Cornelius Mr C. W. M.
Cornelius Mr R. J.
Cornett Mr J. A.
Cornish Mr Mike
Corrigan-Clark Mrs T.
Cosgrove Mr D. J. S.
Costello-Haloute Mrs Suzanne
Cotswold Racing & Lambourn Horse
Cotswold Stud
Cottingham Mr C. **50**
Cottle Mrs P. M.
Cotton Mrs Rowena
Cottrell Mr A. J.
Cottrell Mr Rupert
Coughlan Mrs Anne
Coughlan Mr T. O.
Coull Mr Gary
Coulson Mr Mick
Count Calypso Racing
Countrywide Racing
Countrywide Steel & Tubes Ltd
Coupe Mr J.
Courage Mr C. J.
Court Mr T. C.
Cousins Mr E.
Cousins Miss S. M.
Coveney Mr Andrew
Coventry Lady Maria
Coventry Countess
Cover Mr J. A.
Cover Point Racing
Cowan Mr G. M.
Cowan Mr Gordon
Coward Mrs C. A.
Cowdray Lord
Cowie Mr R.
Cowl Mrs Linda
Cowley Mr R. W.
Cox Mr C.R.
Cox Mr David H. **51**
Cox Mr David
Cox Mrs T. L.
Cox Mr Timothy
Coyle Miss Bridget
Crabb Mr R. K.
Craddock Mr Alan G.
Craddock Mr K.
Craggs Mrs K.
Craig Mr B. J.
Craig Miss I. E. L.
Crake Mr R. J.
Crandon Park Stud
Crane Mr I. P.
Crate Mr Peter M.
Crawford-Smith Mr N. L.
Crawght-Green Mrs A.
Crawshaw Mrs A. F. B.
Crawshaw Lord
Craze Miss J. F
Cree Lodge Racing Club
Crichton-Watt Mr David
Crichton Mr J.M.
Cricketers Club Owners Group (2000)
Crockett Major J. R.
Croft Mrs P. D.
Crook Mr A. D.
Crossley Cooke Mr C.

Crossley Cooke Mrs E. A. G.
Crowley Miss Jo
Crutchley Mr R. **52**
Cuadra Africa
Cuddihy Mr Richard G.
Cullinan Mr J. M.
Cumani Mrs Luca
Cumbrian Industrials Ltd
Cundell Mr P. D.
Cunliffe-Lister Mrs S.
Cunningham Mr T. S. M.
Cunningham-Brown Mr K. O.
Cunningham-Reid Mr M.
Curley Mrs B. J.
Curling Mrs Peter
Curry Mr T.
Curry Mr T. M. J.
Curtis Mr Charles
Curtis Mr T. M.
Curzon The Hon. R.F.N.
Cushing Mr H. A.
Cussons Mr S. H.
Cuthbert Mrs Bernice M.
Cuthbert Mr T. A. K.
Cyzer Mr C. A.
Cyzer Mrs Charles

D

D. Goodenough Removals & Transport **52**
D.R. Gandolfo Ltd
Dab Hand Racing
Dachel Stud
Dakin Mr O.P.
Dalby Mr P.C.J **53**
Dale Mr J.S.
Dale Mrs Jenny
Dale Mr M.L.
Dales Mr P.A.
Dalgety Mrs Hugh
Dalgleish Mr Ian G.M.
Dalmeny Lord
Dalton Mrs Heather
Dalton Mr J.N.
Daly Mr D.J.
Daly Mr M. A. J.
Danebury Racing Stables Ltd
Daniel Mrs A.
Daniels Mr J.
Daniels Mrs R. J.
Danum Racing
Darby Mr John
Darby Mr K. H.
D'Arcy Mr Paul
D'Arcy Mrs Sue
Daresbury Lord
Darling Mr D.W.D.
Darling Mr Paul
Darling Mr W.
Darlington Mr R.
Darlington Mrs Sylvia
Dartnall Mr V.R.A.
Dascombe Mr B.
Dasmal Mr Khalifa
Davall Mrs John **54**
Davenport Mrs J.V.C.
Davies Mrs Chris
Davies Mr F.

Davies Mr H.J.W.
Davies Mr Mel
Davies Mr O.I.F.
Davies Dr T.J.W.
Davies Mr Twelly
Davis Mr J.G.V.
Davis Sir Peter
Davis Mr. Peter N.
Davis Mr Scott H.
Davis Mr Susan
Davis Mr Tim
Davis Mr Warwick
Davis Lady
Davison Mrs Gail
Davison Major Paddy
Davison Mr R.C.
Dawes Mrs A.E.
Dawson Mrs A
Dawson Mr M.J.
Dawson Mr Tom
Day Mr A.A.
Day Mr Adam
Day Mr G.E.
Day Mr J.F.
Day Mrs Lee Ann
Daykin Mr Pete
de Beau-Lox Mr Ronnie **55**
de Best-Turner Mr W.
De Burgh Mr H.
de Burgh Major J.H.
De Chair Miss Helena
De Chambure Marc
de Giles Mr J.A.T.
De La Haye Mr Les
De La Warr Lady
De La Warr Lord
De La Warr Racing
De Las Casas Mr J.
De Lisle Wells Mr J.
De Plumpton Hunter Mr E.P.F.
de Plumpton Hunter Mr R.T.
De Rothschild Sir Evelyn
De Savary Mr Nicholas
De Savary Mrs Nicholas
De Vere Hunt Mr P.
de Wesselow Mr Ian
de Wesselow Mrs L.S.R.
Deacon Mr Dennis
Deakin Mr A.J.
Deal Mr P.A.
Dean Mr F.
Dean Mr Nigel
Dean Mr Richard
Dean Ivory Racing Ltd
Dearman Mr Guy
Deen Mr K.E.
Deer Mr D.J. **56**
Deer Mr P.J.
Delahooke Mr J.S.
Delaney Mr Martin
Dempsey Mr G.E.
Dempster Mr Nigel
Denmark Mr Malcolm C.
Dennis Mr D.S.
Dennis Mr D.W.
Dennis Mr Toby E.D.
Dennis Mr W.W.
Derby Lord
Derby The Countess of
Desmond Mr D.F.
Deuters Mr Chris

Devine Mrs Anne
Devine Mrs M.
Devon The Earl of
Devonshire Duke of
Dewar-Finch Mrs S.
Dextra Lighting Systems
Dhobiwallah Racing
Diamandis Mrs Sarah J.
Diamond Mr Peter
Diamond Racing Limited
Dibb Mr Sam
Dick Mrs R.
Dicken Mr A.R.
Dickinson Mr F.A.
Dig In Racing
Digby Mrs R.E. **57**
Dill Mrs R.P.G.
Dilley Mr Robert W.
Dillon Mrs J.D.
Dilnott-Cooper Mrs R.M.
Dilworth Mr E.G.
Dilworth Mr F.J.
Dimmock Mr Peter
Dix Mr A.B.
Dixey Mr Charles
Dixon Mrs M.E.
Dixon Mr M.H.
Dixon Mr Paul J.
Dixon Mr R.
Doble Mr G.A.
Dobney Mr Russell
Dobson Mr D.H.W.
Dobson Mrs P.J.
Dobson Mr W.J.
Dod Mrs P.
Dodd Mrs Peter M.
Dodds Mr J.P.
Doel Mr G.
Doel Mrs R.
Doherty Mr Thomas
Doherty Mr W.
Dolby Mr J.W.
Domino Racing
Done Mrs Mo
Donner Mrs P.
Donoughmore Lord **58**
Donoughue Lord
Donovan Mr Jamie
Donovan Mr P.
Donworth Mr Bobby
Dooley Mr J.G.
Dore Mr M.A.
Dorji H.E. Lhendup
Dorrington Mr T.G.
Dorrington Mr V.P.
Doubleprint
Douglas Mr P.J.
Douglas, Davis, Urquhart
Douglas-Pennant Mrs D.M.
Douglas-Pennant Miss S.
Dowse Mr I.
Doyle Mr J.T.
Doyle Mr K.
Doyle Mr M.
Doyle Mrs Sally
Doyle Sam
Doyle Miss S.J.
Drabble Mr J.L.
Dragonchain Partnership
Dragon's Stud
Drake Mr D.A.

Drake Mr M.J.
Draper Mr Alan
Dream Makers Partnership
Dresher Mrs L.M.
Drew Mr C. **59**
Driscoll Mr D.H.
Druce Mrs J.
Drury Mr D.M.
Drysdale Mr J.C.
Drysdale Mr Robert
Du Pre Miss I. D.
Dubai Thoroughbred Racing
Duckett Mr Brian
Duckhaven Stud
Duckworth Mr J.
Duddy Mr John
Dudley Mr W.E.
Duff Gordon Lady
Duffield Mrs Ann
Duffy Mr Hugh M.
Dufosee Mr J.W.
Dugdale Sir William
Duggan Mr E.P.
Duggan Mr J.D.
Duggan Mr John
Duke Mr A.
Duke Mr B.
Dukes Mr O.R.
Dun Mr J.M.
Dunbar Mr Ian
Duncan Mrs John
Dundas Lady
Dune Racing
Dunford P.J.
Dunleavy Dr Michael **60**
Dunlop Mrs Edward
Dunlop Mr J.L.
Dunn Mrs A.J.K.
Dunn Mr B.
Dunn Mrs C.J.
Dunn Mr D.
Dunn Sir Robin
Dunne Mr David J.
Dunne Mrs V.A.J.
Dunning Mrs Margaret R.
Dupont Mr C.W.W.
Durham Lord
Durkan Mr Danny
Durkan Mr William
Durkan Limited
Durrant Mr R.J.
Dutfield Mr H.
Dutfield Mrs Nerys
Dutton Mrs Janet
Dutton Mr P.C.
Duxbury Miss Betty
Dwyer Mrs Jane
Dwyer Mr John
Dwyer Mrs Shelley
Dye Mrs J.
Dyer Mrs Katie
Dyer Mrs Linda
Dyson Miss C.
Dyson Mr John

E

Eagle Miss Caroline **61**
Eastwell Manor Racing Ltd

Eastwood Mr W.H.
Eaton Miss Judy
Eclipse Thoroughbreds
Ecosse Racing
Ecurie Pharos
Ecurie Wildenstein
Ecurie Wildenstein (second colours)
Eddery Mrs J.E.
Eddings Mr J.
Edgington Mr C.L.A.
Edgington Mr W.A.
Eddis Mr J.L.
Eddy Mr D.
Eddy Mr R.G.
Eden Mr Charles
Eden Racing
Edge Mr Jeremy
Edinburgh Racing Club
Edmondson Mrs V.M.
Edmunds Mrs S.K.
Edwards Mr Neil J.
Edwards-Heathcote Capt E.J.
Edwards-Heathcote Mrs J.
Egan Mrs Joan L.
Egan Mr John W.
Egerton Mr Charles
Eggleston Mr N.
Egloff Mrs S.
Eich Mr C.P. **62**
El Azar Nagy
Elbrick Estates
Eldon Stud Racing
Elias Miss Shirley
Eliot Mr S.F.
Elite Racing Club
Elite Racing Club (second colours)
Elliot Mr Alan C.
Elliot Mr Andrew
Elliot Mr J.M.
Elliot Mr N.
Elliot Mr Nick
Ellis Mrs A.
Ellis Mr A.P.
Ellis Mrs Angela
Ellis Mrs E.K.
Ellis Mr J.
Ellis Stud Partnership
Ellison Mr Brian
Ellison Racing
Ells Mrs C.J.
Elphick Mrs S.P.
Elsworth Mr D.R.C.
Elsworth D.S.
Elwell Mr R.S.
Embiricos Ms A.E.
Embiricos Mr S.N.J.
Embiricos Mrs S.N.J.
Emery Mrs Jill
Eminence Grice Partnership **63**
Emmerson Mr A.
Emmerson Mr N.M.
Endersby Mrs John
Engelhard (H) Mr C.
England Miss E.M.V.
English Mr David
Ennis Mrs Jean
Epsom Partnership
Equiname Ltd
Erwin Mr David
Espirit de Coprs Racing

Gaskell Mr R.F.U.
Gaskell, Maccioni, Myers & Tregoning
Gates Mr Michael
Gaucci Mr Alessandro
Gee Mr Brian
Gee Mr Colin
Gee Mrs S. M.
Gegg Mr Simon
Gennard Mr Derek
Gent Mr J. A.
Gent Mr Peter
Geoff Hubbard Racing **73**
George Capt. J. A.
George Miss K.
George Mr Edward St
George Mr T. R.
George Mrs C. A. B. St
Georgiou Mr Kalli
Gestut Schlenderhan
Gethin Mr V.Y.
Ghowais Mr Hamad Al
Gibbon Mr D. H.
Gibbons Mr Robbert
Gibbs Mr A. G.
Gibbs Sir Roger G.
Gibson Mr Gary
Gibson Fleming Miss Anthea
Gibson Fleming Mrs W. H.
Gibson, Goddard, Hamer & Hawkes
Gichero Mr D. H.
Gichero Mr Mark
Gidley Wright Mrs N.
Gifford Mrs J.T.
Gifford Mr Michael
Gifford Mr Reg
Gigginstown House Stud
Gilchrist Mr Allan
Gill Mrs J.
Gill Mr Jonathan
Gillespie Dr Anne J. F.
Gillespie Mr F.
Gillett Mr J.A. **74**
Gilmour Mrs Susan
Gilmour Mrs V.
Gingell Mr G. F.
Gingell Mr M. J.
Girls on Tour
Girsonfield Ltd
Girsonfield Stud Racing
Gittings-Watts Mrs M. J.
Given Mrs D.
Gladdis Mr Robert A.
Glasgow House Racing Syndicate
Gleadhill House Stud Ltd
Gleason Mr M.
Glebe House Stud Ltd
Gleeson Mr Eddie
Glover Mr Graham R.
Glover Mr J. A.
Godbere_Dooley Mrs L. R.
Goddard Mr Arthur
Goddard Mrs Linda
Goddard Miss Lorna
Godfrey Mrs Helen
Godfrey Mr Lionel
Godolphin
Godolphin (second colours)
Goess-Saurau Count K.
Goess-Saurau Countess

Gold Group International Ltd
Golden Furlong Racing
Goldie Mr J. S. **75**
Goldie's Friends
Goldsmith Lady Annabel
Goldsmith Mr B.
Goldsmith Mr B.J.
Gollings Mrs Jayne M.
Gollings Mr S.
Gomersall Mr Raymond
Gompertz Mr Jeremy
Good Mr J. R.
Goodbody Mr Michael
Goodbody Mrs R.
Goode Mrs C. M.
Goode Mr Graham
Goodman Mr A. A.
Goodman Mr D. J.
Goodman Mrs Patricia
Goodwood Racehorse Owners Group
Gordon Franks Training
Gordon-Watson Mr C.
Gordon Mrs Fiona
Gordon-Watson Miss M.
Gore-Andrews Mrs R. W.
Goring Hotel
Gosden Mr John H. M.
Gosling Mrs Miles
Gosling Mrs T.
Goulandris Mr P. G.
Gover Mr Bernard
Gower Mr David
Grace Mr M. J. **76**
Graff Mr Markus
Graham Mr A. B.
Graham Mr Doug
Graham Mrs Douglas
Graham Mr J. D.
Graham Mr N. R. H.
Graham Mr William
Graham Mr A.
Granite By Design Ltd
Grant Mr Chris
Grant Mr John C.
Grassick Mr L. P.
Gray Mr B. M.
Gray Mr Frederick
Gray Mr Peter
Gray Mr R. E.
Gray Mr Robert
Grazebrook Mr A. M.
Great Head House Estates Ltd
Greatorex Mr R. E.
Gredley Mrs R. J.
Gredley Mr T. C. O.
Gredley Mr W. J.
Gredley (second colours) Mr W.J.
Green Lady
Green Mr C. R.
Green Mr Charles
Green Mr David A.
Green Mr Jack
Green Mr R. Lycett **77**
Green Mr M. E.
Green Mrs N. J. G.
Green Mr Paul
Green (second colours) Mr Paul
Green Mr Raymond Anderson
Green Sir Simon Lycett
Green Mr T. A.

Green Mr T. J.
Greenall Hon Mrs J.
Greenbay Stables Ltd
Greenfield Stud
Greenwood Mr A.
Greenwood Mr J. J.
Greenwood Major Paul
Greenwood Mr R. E. S.
Greetham Mr J. M.
Gregson Mr G. G. A.
Greig Mrs C. G.
Greig Mrs D. C.
Greig Colonel D.C.
Greig Mr Neil
Grenville-Webb Mr R.
Greystoke Stables Ltd
Griffin Mr A. P.
Griffin Mr Reg
Griffiths Mrs E. F.
Griffiths Mr G. E.
Griffiths Mr Richard
Griffiths Mr S. G.
Grimston Mrs J. M. **78**
Grimston The Hon G. C. W.
Grimthorpe (H) Lord
Grinter Mr A.
Grissell Mr D. M.
Grosvenor Lady Jane
Group 1 Racing (1994) Ltd
Gruber Mr Rubin
Grundy Bloodstock Limited
Gryffindor (www.racingtours. co.uk)
Guerin Mr B. M.
Guest Mr I.
Guest Mr John
Guest Mr Rae
Guillambert Mrs J. L.
Gulliver Mrs P. D.
Gunn Mrs J. J. T.
Gunn Mr Robert
Guthrie Mr Alan
Guthrie Mr J. A.
Gutkin Mr J. S.
Gutner E & Krysztoflack Racing (H)
Guy Mrs Vicki
Guyer Mr Douglas
Gyle-Thompson Mr D. C. G.

H

H. K. Commissions **79**
Habershon-Butcher Mr J.T.
Haberson-Butcher Mr J.T.
Hackett Mrs Monica
Hacking Mrs Nan
Hadden-Wight Mrs J.
Hadjioannou Mr A.
Haggas Mr B.
Haggas Mrs M. M.
Haggas Mr M. R.
Haggas Mr R.
Haggas Mr W. J.
Haigh Mrs A.J.
Haigh Miss V.
Haine Mrs Diana
Haine Mr G.
Haines Mr W.V.

Hales Mr J.
Hales Miss L.
Halewood International Ltd
Halford Mr J. M. F.
Halifax Lady
Halifax Lord
Hall Mr Peter
Hall Farm Racing
Haloute Dr A.
Haloute Mr Elias
Halsall Mr D. A.
Ham Mr G. A.
Hambro Mr Richard **80**
Hambro Mrs R. E.
Hambro Mr Rupert
Hamer Mr C. M.
Hamilton House Limited
Hamilton Park Members Syndicate
Hammond Mrs Alex
Hammond Mr B. P.
Hammond Mr J.
Hammond Mr M. D.
Hammond Mr Michael A.
Hanbury Mr B.
Hanbury Mrs Ben
Hanbury Major Christopher
Hanbury Mrs Christopher
Hanbury Mr E. R.
Hanbury Mrs M. A.
Hanbury Capt T. F. J.
Hancock Mr Jeremy
Hancock III (H) Mr Arthur B.
Hand Mr Reg
Hand Mr Richard
Hand Mr Richard
Hanmer Mr John
Hanmer Bt Sir John
Hannon Mrs J. A.
Hannon Mr R.
Hannon Mr T.
Hanson Mr J.
Hanson The Hon Robert
Harcourt-Wood Mrs B.
Hardcastle Mrs J. A. S. **81**
Harding The Hon Miss D.
Harding Mr R. L.
Hardy Mr Chris
Hardy Sir Richard
Hardy Lady
Harland Mr I.
Harlequin Racing
Harlequin Software Consultants
Harley Mr J. E.
Harper Mr C. J.
Harrap Mr Simon
Harries Lt-Col E. K.
Harries Mr E. L.
Harries Mr W. C.
Harrington Lady
Harrington Lord
Harris Mrs A. E.
Harris Major J. D.
Harris Lady
Harris Mr H.R.
Harris, Clark, Swinburn & Harris
Harrison Mr Neil
Harrison Mrs Pat
Harrison Mr Ray
Harrison Mr S. J.
Harrison Mr S.R.
Harrison Lady

Harrison Major N. J.
Harrison-Allan Mr W. A.
Harrison-Burcombe Mr B.   **82**
Harry Dunlop Racing Partnership
Hartigan Miss D. M.
Hartigan Mr G. C.
Hartingdon (H) Lord
Hartley Ms A.
Hartley Miss Freya
Hartley Mr O. R. M.
Hartley Mrs P.A.H.
Hartnell Mrs D.
Harvey Mrs Belinda
Harvey Mr H. F. Craig
Harwood Mrs G.
Harwood Mrs M. J.
Haslam Mr P. C.
Haslam Mrs V.
Haslam Mrs Wendy
Hastings Mrs P.
Hastings Sir Stephen
Hastings-Bass Mr S.
Hathaway Mr Bernard
Hatta Bloodstock International Ltd
Havelock Racing
Hawke Mr N. J.
Hawkins Mrs B. M.
Hawkins Mr J.
Hawkins Mr K. R. W.
Hawkins Mr Tim
Haydn-Jones Mr D.
Haydn-Jones Mrs E. M.
Haydock Park National Hunt
Partnership
Haydon Mr J. W.   **83**
Hayes Mrs Brendan
Hayes Mr J.
Haynes Mrs Denis
Haynes Mrs H. E.
Hayward Major J. R.
Hayward Mr Tony A.
Hayward (H) Lady
Head Mr Alec
Head Viscount
Headquarters Partnership
Heaney Mr A.
Heaney Mr J.
Heaney Mr S.R.J.
Heart of the South Racing
Heath Mr A. M.
Heath Mr Christopher
Heath Mr D.
Heathcote Mr Robert
Heathcote Mr W.
Heaton Mr Mark
Heber-Percy The Hon Mrs A. E.
Heber-Percy Mrs Alan
Hedditch Mr Richard
Hedger Mr P. R.
Hedlund Mrs L.
Heeru Kirpalani Racing
Heffernan Mr Patrick
Heimann The Hon Mrs D.
Heinz Mrs H. J.
Helaissi Mr A. S.   **84**
Helena Springfield Ltd
Heler Mr Joseph
Hellwood Stud Farm
Hellyer Mr B. G.
Hellyer Mrs E. G.
Hely-Hutchinson Mr T. M.

Hemmings Mr Robert
Hemmings Mr Trevor
Hemmings (second colours)
Mr Trevor
Hemphill Lord
Hemstock Mr S.D.
Henderson Mr H.
Henderson Mrs John
Henderson Mr N. J.
Hendi Mr Mohammed Bin
Henriques Mr M.
Henry Mrs R.
Herbert Mr Ivor
Herbert Mrs Sarah
Herbert The Hon H.
Hern (H) Mrs W. R.
Herries Lady
Hersey-Walker Mr John
Hertford Offset Limited
Heseltine Mr T. W.
Hesmonds Stud
Hetherington Mr John
Hetherton Mr J.
Heyes Mr A. J.
Heywood Mr Michael   **85**
Hiatt Mr P.W.
Hibberd Mr Dick
Hibbert-Foy Mr P. M. L.
Hickey Mr C. R.
Hickey Miss E.
Hickman Mr Andrew
Hickman Mrs D. M.
Hickman Mr J. C.
Hickman Mr P. J.
Hickman Mr Richard
Hickman (H) Mr J.C.S.
Hicks Mr David
Higgin Mr M. E. S.
Higgins Mr C. G.
Higgins Mrs D. J.
Higham Mr B.
Highclere Thoroughbred Racing
Highclere Thoroughbred Racing
(second colours)
Higson Mr K.
Hilal Mr Mohammed
Hill Mr J. Ward
Hill Mr Martin
Hills Mr B. W.
Hills Mrs B. W.
Hills Mr Charles
Hills Mrs J.
Hills Mr J. W.
Hills Mrs M.
Hill-Walker Mr P. A
Hill-Wood Mr I. C.   **86**
Hinchcliffe Mrs Mandy
Hinde Mrs Tim
Hindley Mrs C. H.
Hindley Mr J. J.
Hindley Mrs S.
Hines Mr Frazer
Hing Mr Yue Yun
Hinojosa Mr Felipe
Hintelsham AB Partners
Hintelsham Cree Partners
Hintelsham DS Partners
Hintelsham SPD Partners
Hintelsham Thoroughbreds
Hirschfeld Mr Tony
Hislop (H) Mrs J.L.

Hitchcott Mr P.D.
Hitchins Mr J. C.
Hitchins Mrs K.
Hitchins Mr N. J.
Hoad Mrs Julie
Hoad Mr R. P. C.
Hobbs Mr A. L.
Hobbs Mr A. R. C.
Hobbs Mrs C.
Hobbs Mr P. D.
Hobbs Mr P. J.
Hobbs Mrs S. L.
Hobby Dr J. A. E.
Hobby Mrs Joy
Hockenhull Mr W. D.   **87**
Hodder Mr J. G.
Hodge Mr A.H.B.
Hodge Mr Alastair
Hodges Mr R. J.
Hoey Mrs M.
Hogarth Mr & Mrs A.
Hogarth Racing
Hoh Oilfield Services Limited
Hoiles Mr Richard
Holdcroft Mr T. G.
Holder Mr Andy
Holder Mr & Mrs Derek & Cheryl
Holder Mrs J
Holder Mr Pete
Holder (second colours) Mr Pete
Holdsworth Mr N. J.
Holistic Racing Ltd
Holland-Martin Mrs E.
Holland-Martin Mr T. D.
Hollands Mrs J. M.
Holliday Mr L. B.
Hollingsworth Mr A.
Hollingsworth Mr Mark
Hollinshead Mr A. N.
Hollinshead Mrs L. A.
Hollinshead Mr R.
Hollowood Mrs Claire
Hollowood Dr John
Holman-Chappell Mrs Anne V.   **88**
Holt Mr Simon
Homebred Racing
Homeizi Mr Saleh Al
Homer-Morris Mr F.
Hon Dr Johnny
Hong Kong Cricket Club
Honourable Artillery Company
Hood Ms Rachel D. S.
Hope Mr F.
Hope Mrs N.
Hope Mr S.R.
Hopetoun The Earl
Horgan Mr C. A.
Horgan Mr James
Horgan Mr Jim
Hornall Mr Archie
Horne Mr Mark
Horne Mrs Mark
Horner Miss L.
Horner-Harker Mr P.A.
Horner-Harker Mrs Sarah
Horsburgh Mr Peter
Hosford-Tanner Mr M.
Houghton Mr Ernie
Houghton Mr George
Howard Mrs B.
Howard Mr Leonard

Howard Barton Stud
Howard-Spink Mr G.
Howard-Vyse Mrs V.   **89**
Howe Mr Dave
Howe Mr S. P.
Howitt, Mr Michael
Howland Jackson Mr A.
Howlett General Sir Geoffrey
Hubbard Mr N. B. F.
Hubbuck Mr J. S.
Hue Williams Mrs C. J.
Huggins Mr R. W.
Hughes Mr Emlyn
Hughes Mr M.T.
Hughes Mr P.
Hughes Mr Paddy
Hughes Mr Rob
Hughes Mr Sebastian F.
Humaid Mr Saeed Abdullah
Humby Mr M. C.
Humphreys Mrs Susan
Humphries-Cuff Mrs Philip
Hunt Mr C. Harman
Hunt Mr J.T.
Hunt & Co (Bournemouth) Ltd
Hunt (H) Mr N. Bunker
Hunter Blair Mr T.
Huntingdon Lord
Hurley Miss Caroline
Hutchinson Mr Dennis
Hutchinson Mr Maurice
Hutsby Mr F. A.
Hutsby Mr K.   **90**
Hyde Mr Derek
Hyde Mr Edward
Hyde Mr T.
Hyde Mrs T. P.

I

Ian David Limited   **90**
Ibbotson Mrs D.
Ilsley Mr A.J.
In The Pink Syndicate
In Touch Partnership
Incisa Don Enrico
Ingham Mr Nik H. B.
Ings Mr Michael H.
Innes Mr Peter
Intersky Corporate Club
Interskyracing.com
Ioannou Mr M.
Iona Equine
Irvine Mr A.
Irvine Mr D.
Irvine Mrs J.
Irving Miss H. M.
Irving Mr L.
Irving Mrs L.
Irving Mr Rupert C.
Irwin Mrs S.
Islanmore Stud
Iveagh Lady
Ivens Mr Bill
Iveson Mr D.F.
Ivory Mr Dean   **91**
Ivory Mrs J. M.
Ivy House Racing
Izamis Mrs P.

J

J Nattrass M Howard R Fawcett T Fawcett **91**
J. B. R. Leisure Ltd
J. Bernstein & C.A. Green
J. Bernstein & C.A. Green (second colours)
Jaber Mr Mohammed
Jabre Mr G.
Jack Brown (Bookmaker) Ltd
Jackson Mr A. A. W.
Jackson Mr Bill
Jackson Mr C. F. C.
Jackson Mr David J.
Jackson Mrs J. A.
Jackson Mr Norman
Jackson Mr W. J. P.
James Mr David
James Mr E.
James Mr Keith
James Mrs M. E
James Mr S. W.
James-Duff Mr D.
Jarvis Mr A. P
Jarvis Mr H. J.
Jarvis Mr John F.
Jarvis Mr M. A.
Jarvis Mr T.
Jarvis Mr William **92**
Jarvis Mrs Ann
Jarvis Mrs Gay
Jarvis Mrs R. N.
Jay Dee Bloodstock Limited
Jebel Ali Racing Stables
Jenkins Mr J. R.
Jenkins Mrs Wendy
Jenks Mrs Bryan
Jenks Mr Bryan P.
Jenks Mr David
Jenks Mr R. J.
Jenks Mrs Richard
Jenks Mr W.
Jenks Mrs W. P.
Jenner Mr J.
Jerdein Mr Charles
Jet UK Limited
Joel (H) Mr H.J.
Joel (H) Mr Stanhope
Jobs Racing
John Humphreys (Turf Accountant)
John Nicholls (Banbury) Ltd
John Wilding Promotions
Johnsey Mrs Margaret
Johnsey Estates (1990) Ltd
Johnson Mr D. A.
Johnson Mr I. K.
Johnson Mr M. R.
Johnson Mr P.
Johnson Mr D.V. **93**
Johnson Mrs Joy
Johnson Mr Mark
Johnson Mr C.R.
Johnson Houghton Miss E.
Johnson Houghton Mr R. F.
Johnson Houghton Mrs R. F.
Johnston Mr G. C.
Jones Mr A. D.
Jones Mr D. G.

Jones Mr Fergus
Jones Dr G.M.Thelwall
Jones Mr J. F.
Jones Mr J.T.
Jones Mr L. Neil
Jones Mr M. G.
Jones Mr N. J.
Jones Mr P.A.
Jones Mr Peter
Jones Mr S. D.
Jones Mr Simon
Jones Mrs Solna Thomson
Jordan Mr D. F.
Jordan Mr F.
Jordan Mr G.
Jordan Mrs M.
Joseph Mr Jack
Joseph Mr K. P.
Joy Miss Alison
Joy & Valentine Feerick
Joyce Mr T. **94**
Jubert Family
Jumeirah Racing
Jumping Jokers
Juniper Stud Racing
Just Good Fun Club

K

K. C. Partnership II **94**
Kalani Partnership
Kan Mr Paul
Kavanagh Mrs A. G.
Kavanagh Mrs Maxine
Kavanagh R. E.
Keane Mr D. P.
Keane Mr M.
Keary Mr P. J.
Keegan Mrs Jean
Keen Racing
Keeys Geoffrey & Donna
Kehoe Mrs F.
Kehoe Mr P. F.
Keighley Mr J. A.
Keir Mrs E.
Kelburn Dorothea, Viscountess
Kelleway Miss Gay
Kelly Mr B. J
Kelly Mr Diarmaid
Kelly Mr G. P. **95**
Kelly Mr Peter
Kelly Mr Tim
Kelsey-Fry Mr John
Kelso Members Lowflyers Club
Kelvin-Hughes Mr R.
Kemp Mr B. C. S
Kemp Mr M.A
Kemp-Gee Mr M. N.
Kendall Mr L. W.
Kendrick Mr G. D.
Kennard Mr L. G.
Kennard Major & Mrs R. B.
Kennard Lady
Kennedy Mr Ian A.
Kennedy Mr J. P.
Kennet Valley Thoroughbreds
Kent Mr F. N.
Kent H.R.H Princess Michael Of
Kenyon Lord

Keogh Mr Michael H.
Keogh Mr R.
Ker Mr David
Ker Mrs Jeremy
Kerman Mr Anthony D.
Kernow Racing
Kerr Mr D. M.
Kerr Mr John
Kerr Mr W. F.
Kerr-Dineen Mr Michael H.
Kessly Mr E. D. **96**
Keswick Sir Chippendale
Keswick Mrs M. E.
Keswick Mr Simon
Kettlewell Mrs E.A.
Key Mr H.
Khaled Mr S.
Khalid Khalifa Al Nabooda Mr
Khamsin Sheikh Ali Abu
Khan Mr John
Khan (H) Mr R. N.
Kidd Mr Gerald
Kilboy Estate
Kilgour Mr Christy
Killoran Mr Bobby
Kilner Mr Mark
Kilpatrick Mr A. S.
Kimber Mr L. G.
Kimberley (H) Lord
Kimmins Mr M. B. J.
Kinane Mr C. M.
Kindersley Mrs G.
Kindersley Mr P.L.
King Mr A. A.
King Mrs A. L. M
King Mr C.O.
King Mr J. W. G.
Kingham Mrs Brian
Kings Troop Royal Horse Artillery
Kingsclere Stud
Kingstone Warren Partners **97**
Kingwood Stud Ltd
Kinloch Arns (Carnoustie) Ltd
Kinnear Mr J. M.
Kinnersley Optimists
Kinsella-Hurley Mrs S. A. J.
Kirby Mr M.V.
Kirk Mr Sylvester
Kirkland Dr A. I.
Kirkwood Mr L.
Kirpalani Mr H. L.
Kitchen Mr K. G.
Kittow Mrs S.
Kittow Mr W. G.
Kleinwort Lady Lucinda
Kley Mrs Audrey
Knight Mr G.W.
Knight Miss H.
Knight Mr J. R.
Knightsbridge BC
Knipe Mr R. F.
Knipe Mrs R. F.
Knocker Miss Linsey
Knott Mr Anthony
Knott Dr Nigel
Knutsford Lady
Kok Mr J. P.
Krishnan Mr Ananda
Krysztofiak Miss A. M.
Krysztofiak (H) Mr M.

Kuwait Racing Syndicate **98**
Kyle Mr R. J.

L

La Trobe Mrs D. A. **98**
Lacey Mr J. M.
Ladbrokes Staff Racing Partnership
Ladds Mrs Samantha
Ladhams Mr David
Lady Bamford & Sangster Family
Lady Blyth
Lady Caffyn-Parsons & Mrs E.E. Dedman
Lady Eliza Mays-Smith
Lady Carolyn Warren & Floors Farming
Lady Whent And Friends
Ladyswood Stud
Ladywood Farm
Lael Stable
Laggan Farm Stud (H)
Laidlaw Mr Stephen
Lake Miss C.
Lake Mrs E.
Lake Mr N. W.
Lake Mr Phil
Laker Sir Freddie
Lalemant Mr Bob
Lambert Mr Stephen
Lambton Mr G.
Lamyman Mrs S.
Lancaster-Smith Mr D. **99**
Lancaster-Smith Mrs J. M.
Lancaster-Smith Mr R. J.
Landi Mr Ettore
Lane Mrs Jane
Langley Mr R.G.
Lanham Miss Audrey
Lanigan Mr Bob
Larkwood Stud
Lascelles Mrs Hugo
Latilla-Campbell Mr C.
Latilla-Campbell Mr Peter
Lavelle Miss E. C.
Lavelle Mr R. J.
Lavelle Mrs R. J.
Lavender Hill Stud L.L. C.
Lawn Thomas
Lawrence Mr M.W.
Lawrence Mrs S.J.
Lawson Mr Robin
Lawson Johnston Miss
Lawson-Croome Mrs C.
Lay Mr B. L.
Layton Mr J.V.
Lazzari Mr J. A.
Le Blond Mr A. J.
Le Mare (H) Mr N.H.
Lea Mr A. E.
Leadbeater Mr Tim
Leader Mrs H. C.
Leat Mr John **100**
Leat Mrs Ann
Leatham Mr G.H.
Leatham Mr Mark A.
Leatham Mr R. G.
Ledger Mr R. R.
Lee Mr F. H.

Lee Mr F. T.
Lee Miss G. T.
Lee Mr Richard
Leech Mr Paul D.
Leech Mrs S.
Lee-Judson Mr N.
Lees Mr David
Lees Mr John
Lees-Jones Mrs C. P.
Leetham Mr C. R.
Legard Mr William
Legard Lady
Legard Sidebottom & Sykes
Legge Mr P. E.
Leigh Mrs Benjamin
Leigh Family The
Leighton Sir Michael
Lennox Mrs David Gordon
Leslie Mr Richard
L'Estrange Mr David
Let's Go Racing
Lets Go Racing I
Lever Mr G. T.
Lever Mr John   **101**
Lever, Alexander, Dallas
Leverhulme (H) Lord
Leveson-Gower Mr A. J.
Levy Mrs H.
Lewinton Lady
Lewis Mr Ben
Lewis Mr Colin
Lewis Mr Jim
Lewis Mr Keith
Lewis, Matthews and Pole
Lewis-Harris Mrs S.
Li Dr Cornel
Liddiard Mr A.
Liddy Mr Michael
Lilburn Mr T. C.
Liles Mr Grahame
Lilley Mrs Claude
Lilley Mr M.R.
Lillingston Mr Luke
Lim Mr J-P.
Lindley Mrs S. E.
Littmoden Mrs Emma
Littmoden Mr Nick
Livock Mr John
Llewellyn Mr B. J.
Lloyd Mr D. M.
Lloyd Mr Justin
Lloyd-Jones Mr J. W. F.
Lloyd-Webber Lady
Loader Mr A. J.   **102**
Loads Mr Keith F. J.
Lochead Mr Ian
Locke Mrs Paul
Lockey Mrs Beryl
Lockhart Mrs Ann
Lockwood Mrs A.
Lockwood Mrs Lesley
Loder Mr D. R.
Loder Sir Edmund
Logan Mrs H. C.
Lomas Mr William
Lomax Mrs J. P.
London Mr Neville
Longhurst Commander Peter
Lonsdale Mr T.
Lonsdale Countess Of
Lonsdale The Earl Of

Lord Clyde Racing
Lord Daresbury & J.E. Greenall
Lord Huffington-Smythe Racing
Lordship Stud
Loriston-Clarke Mrs A. G.
Lostford Manor Stud
Loudon Mrs John
Louisville Syndicate
Lovat Mrs A.
Love Mr Alan
Lovell Mrs L. R.
Low Mr I. A.
Lowe Mr D.   **103**
Lowe Mr Gary
Loyd C. L., M. C.
Loze Mr A.
Luard Mrs R.
Luard Mr T. P. M.
Lucayan Stud
Lucey Mr Sean
Lucey-Butler Mrs E.
Lucie-Smith Mr D. A.
Luck Mr Guy
Luck Mr N. E. F.
Luders-Gibbs Mr R. E.
Lumsden Mr J. G.
Lumsden Capt. J. M. G.
Luna Bloodstock
Lundberg-Young Mrs Kin
Lundgren Miss J. L.
Lungo Mrs Barbara
Lusardi Mr Tony
Lusty Mrs O. M.
Luttman-Johnson Mrs W. M.
Lyburn Mr A. S.
Lysaght Mr Cornelius

M

M. C. S. D. Racing Ltd   **103**
M. G. Racing
Macalister Mrs B.
Maccioni Mr Alvaro
Macdonald-Buchanan Mr A. J.   **104**
Macdonald-Buchanan Mrs A. J.
Macdonald-Buchanan Mr A. R.
Macdonald-Buchanan Capt J.
Macdonald-Buchanan Mrs S. A.
MacEchern Mr Gavin
MacEwan Mr A. G.
MacGregor I. R. K.
MacGregor Miss M.I.
Mackenzie Mr J. D. H.
Mackenzie Mr K. C. B.
Mackenzie Mr M. G.
Mackie Mrs J.
Macleod Mr J.
MacNair Mr R.M.J.
MacPherson Mrs Janis
Macready Sir Nevil
Mactaggart Mrs A. H.
Mactaggart Mr B.
Mactaggart Mrs K. B.
Magnier Mrs John
Magnier (second colours) Mrs John
Magnier Miss K.
Magor Mr Philip
Maguire Mr Billy

Maher Mr Peter
Mahmoud Dr Carla
Maitland-Carew The Hon Gerald
Maitland-Jones Mrs Hugh
Makin Mr R. G.
Makin Mrs P.J.
Maktoum Mr Saeed
Al Maktoum   **105**
Maktoum Sheikh Ahmed Bin Saeed Al
Malam Mr D. A.
Malbon Mr N.
Mallen Mr A.
Mallya Mr Vijay
Manana Mr Saeed
Mangan Mr E. J.
Mann Mrs C. J.
Mann Mr Charlie
Mann Mr David
Mann Mr G.
Mann Mr I. R.
Mann Mrs J. M.
Mann Mrs M.
Manton Lady Mary
Manton Lord
Mapletoft Mr Simon
Marchwood Lady
Marchwood Lord
Marfell Mrs M.
Margadale Lady
Margadale Lord
Marinopoulos Mr L.
Mark Johnston Racing Ltd
Mark Kilner Racing Syndicates
Marker Mr Richard
Marks Mr D.
Marks Mr Ian
Marlborough Duke Of
Marlborough Racing Partnership   **106**
Marner (H) Mr C.
Marsden Mr Barry
Marsden Mr J. L.
Marsh Mrs Henry
Marsh Mrs Jennifer
Marsh Mrs M. K.
Marsh Mr S. P.
Marshall Mr B. C.
Marshall Mr Doug
Marshall Mr K.
Marston Stud
Marten The Hon Mrs M. A.
Martin Mr C. M.
Martin Mr Gilbert
Martin Mr Glenn
Martin Mr N.
Martin Mr C.M.
Marvin Mrs M. A.
Mary Reveley Racing Club
Mascalls Stud
Masini Dr Mario
Mason Mr A. J.
Mason Mr A. M.
Mason Mr Paddy
Mason Mr R. G. P.
Masons Arms Racing Club
Masood Mr Hadi
Massereene Lord
Matalon Mr Vernon Carl
Materna Mr G.D.P.
Matham Investments   **107**

Mathias Mrs J.
Matthews Mr F. J.
Matthews Mr F. L.
Matthews Mr R. H. F.
Matthews Mrs S. J.
Matthews Mrs T. S.
Matthews Breeding and Racing
Maude Mrs Sue
Maxse Mr John
Maxse Mrs S.
Maxwell Mrs G. C.
May Mr H. S.
May Mr J. J.
Maynard Mrs Judy
Maynard Mr N. W. E
Maynard Mr P. G. B.
Mayo Mrs J. M.
Mays-Smith Lady Eliza
McAllister Mr B.
McAlpine Mr Adrian N. R.
McAlpine Mrs R.
McAuliffe Mr K. W. J.
McCain Mr D.
McCain Mrs D.
McCalmont Mr Harry R. D.
McCalmont Mr Hugh
McCalmont Mr M. R.
McCalmont Mr P. J.
McCalmont Mr Peter V.
McCarthy Mrs Susan   **108**
McCormack Mr C.
McCormack Mrs D.
McCoy's Neighbours
McCrea Mrs G. E.
McCreery Mr R. J.
McDonald Mrs Susan
McEntee Mrs B. A.
McEntee Mrs R. L.
McEvoy Mr Colm
McFadzean Miss L.
McFarlane Mrs R. M.
McGarrigle Mr B. A.
McGarrigle Mr Luke
McGaughey Mrs E.
McGovern Mr T. P.
McGowan Lady
McGrath Sir Brian
McGrath Mr Jack
McGrath (second colours) Mr Jack
McGuinness Mr G.
McGuinness Mr G. M.
McInnes Mr Ian
McInnes Mr I. W.
McInnes Skinner Mrs F. D.
McInnes Skinner Mrs M.
McInnes Skinner Mrs T. J.
McKay Mr Willie
McKeever Mrs Susie
McKenzie-Coles Mr W. G.
McKinnon Mr J.   **109**
McLain Dr B. I.
McLaren Mr Jim
McMahon Mrs J
McMahon Mr John
McMahon Mr P.
McMahon Mr Peter
McManus Mr J. P.
McNeill Mr J. W.
McNeill Mrs Jill
McNeill Mrs M.
McNeill Mr P.

McNeill Mr Raymond
McPhee Mr Stuart
McSwiney Mr P. J.
Mead Mr Rex L.
Meade Mr Martyn
Mears Group Plc
Meddler Bloodstock
Meddler Racing
Meddler Stud
Meehan Mr B. J.
Meehan (second colours) Mr B. J.
Mellon (H) Mr P.
Melotti Mr Peter
Melville Mr John
Men Behaving Badly
Menzies Miss Janet
Mercer Mr Darren C.
Mercer Mr K. J.
Mercer Mr Stuart M.   110
Meredith Mrs Michael
Meredith Mr R.
Merrick Mr S. J.
Merthyr Motor Auctions
Merza Mr A.
Messinger Stud Limited
Metcalfe Miss C.
Metcalfe Mr David T. J.
Meynell Mr T. G.
Meyrick Sir George
Michael Capt Alex
Michael Miss H.
Michael Howitt & R.C. Davison (under Howitt, Michael etc)
Michaelson Mr R. P. B.
Michell Mr Joe
Midd Shire Racing
Middlebrook Mr G.
Middleham Park Racing
Middleham Park Racing
Middleton Mr Andy
Middleton Mr B. D.
Middleton Mr Keith
Middleton Mr Nicholas D.
Middleton Mr P. J.
Midgley Mrs K. L.
Mikado Syndicate
Milbourne Lodge Partnership
Milburn Mr David
Mildmay-White Mr A.
Mildmay-White Mrs A.
Mildmay-White Mr R.
Miles Mr R.   111
Milham Mr S.A.M.
Milham Mrs S.J.
Millard Mrs Bunty
Millard Mr Derek
Miller Miss D.
Miller Sir Peter
Miller/Richards Partnership
Miller-Bakewell Mr Robert
Milligan Mr & Mrs A.G.
Milligan Mrs G.
Million In Mind Partnership
Million in Mind Partnership
Millman Mr B. R.
Mills Mr A. J.
Mills Mr B. C.
Mills Major D. N.
Mills Mr T. G.
Mills Mrs T. G.
Milmo Mr Patrick

Milner Mr A.
Milton Park Stud
Milward Mr Roger
Minster Stud
Minton Mr D.
Minty Mr Barry
Mitchell Mr J.R.
Mitchell Mr M.
Mitchell Mr M. H.
Mitchell Mr N. R.
Mitchell Mr Philip
Mitchell Mrs D.   112
Mitchell Mrs Jean
Mitford-Slade Mrs P. B.
Mobberley Manor Racing
Mobley Mrs Helen
Moffatt Mrs Y.
Moffatt Mr A.J. & Mrs A.
Mohammed Sheikh
Mohammed (second colours) Sheikh
Mohan Mr T.
Mollers Racing
Molony Mr C. D.
Monaghan Mr James
Monarch Thoroughbreds
Monteith Mr P.
Moody Mrs M.E.
Moody Miss R. A.
Moody Mr R. C.
Moore Mr G.
Moore Mr R. A. A.
Moore Mr Stan
Moore Mrs Susan
Moore Mrs T.
Moore Mr T. W.
Moran Mrs Elga
Moran Mr Joe
Morant Mr John
Moratalla Marquesa de
Mordaunt-Smith Mrs A. S.
Morgan Mr H. R.
Morgan Mr W. G. N.   113
Morgan-Jones Mr Rhydian
Moriarty Mr Michael
Moriarty Mr P. J.
Moriarty Mrs Teresa M.
Morley Mr A.
Morley Mrs M. F. D.
Morley Mrs Sylvia
Morlock Mr C. P. H.
Morris Mr D.
Morris Mr H. F.
Morris Mr J.
Morris Mrs Hugo
Morris Mr P. H.
Morris Mr Paul
Morris Mr W. D.
Morrison Mr D.
Morrison Mr H.
Morrison Mr M. J.
Morton Mr A. L. R.
Morton Mr C. J.
Morton Mr James
Moss Mr Brian
Moss Mr Derrick
Moss Mr Eddie
Moss Mrs Jill
Mould Mr H. R.
Mould Mr Russ
Moulden Mr J. P.

Mountain Lady
Mountain Miss Debbie   114
Mountain Sir Denis
Mountbatten Lord Ivar
Mountgrange Stud
Mourad Mr Nabil
Moyglare Stud Farm
Mrs Sarah Diamandis & Mrs Celia Woollett
Mrs Thomas Wallis & Her Family
Mulholland Mr Brian
Mulholland Mr M.
Mullineaux Mr Michael
Mullins Mrs Sally
Mullins Mr Seamus
Mulryan Mr S.
Munro-Wilson Mr Broderick
Murdoch Mr W.
Murphy Mr C.J.
Murphy Mr P. G.
Musgrave Mr N.P.C.
Musker Lady Rose
Musson Mr W. J.
Mustoe Mr N.
Myers Mr David
Myers Mr Gerald
Myers Mr Martin
Myers Mrs Nicole
Mystic Meg Limited

N

Nagle Mrs David   115
Napier Mr D.
Napier Mrs N.
Nass Mr Fawzi Abdulla
National Hunt Partnership
Naylor Mr Bill
Naylor Mr D.
Naylor-Leyland Sir P.V.
Nazar Mr Mohamad Razif
Neardown Stables
Neaves Mr B.
Needham Mr A. E.
Needham Mr J. L.
Needham Mr P.
Neill Mr Terry
Neilson Mr H.W.
Nelmes-Crocker Mr M.
Nelson Mrs Liz
Nelson Mr Peter
Nelson Mr W. M.
Nesbitt Mrs John
Nesfield Mr C.V.
Network Racing
Network Training
Nevison Mr D. S.
Newbury Racehorse Owners Club
Newbury Racehorse Owners Group
Newbyth Stud
Newcombe Mr A. G.
Newell Miss H. M.
Newgate Stud
Newick Park Partnership   116
Newland Mr D.
Newman Mr J. W.
Newman Mr Nick

NewmarketConnections.com
Newsells Park Stud
Newton Mr Philip
Ng Mr M.
Ng Mr Michael
Ng Mr Robert
Niarchos Mrs Maria I.
Niarchos Mr Spyros
Niarchos Mr Philip S.
Niarchos Family
Nicholls Ms Bridget
Nicholls Mr Paul
Nicholson Mr David
Nicholson Mr Keith
Nicolson Mr M.
Nielsen Mr B. E.
Nigel & Carolyn Elwes
Niven Mr P. D.
Nock Mr Gerard
Noodles Racing
Norcroft Park Strud
Norman Mr H.G.
Normandie Stud Ltd
North Farm Stud
North West Racing Club
North Lodge Racing Club
Northmore Stud   117
Northumberland The Duke of
Northumberland Jumpers
Norton Mr J.
Norton Mr Rex
Norton Mr W. E.
Norton House Racing
Notalotterry
Nugent Mr C.R.
Nugent Sir John
Nugent Mr O.
Nunn Mr S.
Nutt Mr C.Y.
Nuttall Mr A. E. S.
Nutting Mr D. A.
Nye Mrs Y. M.

O

Oakhill Wood Stud   117
Oaksey Lord
Oakview Racing
Obaida Mr Mohamed
O'Brien Mr D. C.
O'Brien Mr K. G.
O'Brien Mr N. J.
O'Brien Mrs V.
O'Brien Lady
O'Callaghan Mrs N.
O'Connor Mr Con   118
O'Connor Mr D.
O'Connor Mr J. P. M.
O'Connor Mr John
Odell Mr W. J.
Odner Mr B.
Ogden C.B.E LLD Sir Robert
O'Grady Mrs Andrea
O'Keeffe Mr Jedd
O'Kelly Major E.
Old Mr J. A. B.
Old Mrs Jim
Old Mr W. R.
Old Berks Partnership

R

V

W

Y

Z

NUMBERS